C000228764

London 2012 Sustainable Design

An official London 2012 publication

London 2012 Sustainable Design

Delivering a Games Legacy

WILEY

Hattie Hartman

Commissioned photography by Edmund Sumner

DEDICATION

To Adam and Gabriela with the hope that they will witness
innovative ways to protect our planet in their lifetimes.

To JT for his energy, insights and companionship, which make
every day richer.

AUTHOR'S ACKNOWLEDGEMENTS

The London 2012 Olympic and Paralympic Games have provided an opportunity for many
of the UK's most creative urban thinkers, architects and engineers to test ideas for sustainable
city-making and low-carbon buildings. I would like to thank all those who met me (see page
253) and responded to my persistent emails during my research for this book. A special
thank you to Dan Epstein for a crucial initial interview that set this work in context, to Kevin
Owens, John Hopkins and Jerome Frost for invaluable site visits in the depths of winter, which
enabled me to experience first-hand the Olympic Park and its venues, and to Jeff Keas at
Populous for prompt replies to countless questions. I am also grateful to Simon Wright, Holly
Knight and Ruari Maybank at the ODA, and Caroline Richards and Christian Bonnard at
CLM, for their time and assistance on the text.

The genesis of this book stems from my work at *The Architects' Journal* over the last five
years, where I have had the privilege of writing about the latest developments in green
building in the UK as they happen. I would like to extend a particular thanks to the *AJ* team
members, who have provided me with flexibility and support during this project.

Throughout the writing process, Helen Castle, my commissioning editor at John Wiley &
Sons Ltd, has provided extraordinarily insightful and detailed comments that have honed and
enlivened the text. My agent, Shelley Power, has also been a steady, supportive presence.
A special thank you is due to my research assistant, Tanisha Raffiuddin, for transcribing hours
of interviews and chasing images with good humour and efficiency. And I am very grateful
to Sosuke Sugiura for his able graphic assistance.

I would also like to thank my family, especially Gabriela, who has offered smiles and
encouragement during my seemingly endless evenings and weekends at the computer over
the last few months. Without their constant support and intuitive understanding, this book
would not have been possible.

Contents

Chapter 1

Towards a Sustainable London 2012

HACKNEY
MARSHES

WALTHAM FOREST

BMX

VELODROME

CHOBHAM FARM
SCHOOL

HOCKEY

BASKETBALL
ARENA

RIVER

MPC

IBC

LEA

OLYMPIC AND PARALYMPIC VILLAGE

IBC/MPC CATERING VILLAGE

RIVER

STRATFORD INTERNATIONAL

HACKNEY

HANDBALL
ARENA

HACKNEY WICK

LEE

STRATFORD CITY
MIXED USE
TOWN CENTRE

HERTFORD UNION CANAL

STRATFORD REGIONAL

WATERPOLO

NAVIGATION

CITY
MILL
RIVER

THE

AQUATICS CENTRE

OLD
RIVER
LEA

WATER
WORKS

OLYMPIC STADIUM

NEWHAM

STRATFORD
HIGH STREET

GREENWAY

RIVER

GREENWAY

TOWER
HAMLETS

PUDDING
MILL LANE

London 2012 is set to redefine what it means to stage the Olympic and Paralympic Games. A spectacular one-off mega-event that mobilises 14,000 plus athletes and millions of spectators from around the world may seem at odds with a sustainable agenda. Yet London has seized the occasion to demonstrate how the Games can be approached differently, confounding preconceived notions about the excesses of such events.

From the outset, the defining mantras of London 2012 have been regeneration and legacy. The extent to which that has been a success is the subject of this book. Every investment and design decision was tested for its ongoing viability after the Olympic Flame moved on. The aspiration was that no venue would be built that did not have a guaranteed long-term use and that the permanent footprint of the Games would enhance the built and natural environment of east London's Lower Lea River Valley and the life opportunities of its residents.

Early discussions about London's hosting the 2012 Games had considered the idea of a west London Games centred around Foster + Partners' Wembley Stadium, under construction at the time. Mayor Ken Livingstone was adamant that if London were to win the Games, then they should be located in east London with urban regeneration at their core. The momentum of the Games could be used to redress the city's long history of economic disparity between its east and west ends.

1 (Previous page) London 2012 Games Masterplan. The majority of new sports venues are located in a new Olympic Park in east London.

2 View of Olympic Park site prior to redevelopment. Criss-crossed by semi-abandoned waterways, the site was occupied by 52 electricity pylons and more than 200 buildings, primarily industrial sheds.

2

Closer to the mouth of the Thames, east London was historically the city's port, characterised by docks, industries related to shipbuilding and the working-class neighbourhoods that support them. It was also the city's service zone, fragmented by large-scale transport and utility infrastructure. West London, favoured by the aristocracy, benefited from generous parks and spacious residential terraces. East London had suffered a serious decline in the second half of the twentieth century when the introduction of container ports resulted in the closure of the docks, which had been the area's primary source of employment. By the turn of the twenty-first century, the proposed Host Boroughs numbered amongst the most economically deprived local authority areas in England.

Of utmost importance throughout the planning for the Games have been the prospects for east Londoners beyond 2012. The hope is to transform this part of east London by transforming a contaminated industrial site into a new green lung, surrounded by employment centres, affordable low-carbon housing and improved community facilities. The new park was intended to enhance the landscape of the Lee Valley Regional Park and connect to the East London Green Grid, a strategy for reinforcing open space in this part of the city. It was this ambitious strategy, combined with a clear sense of environmental responsibility, which helped London to emerge victorious at the International Olympic Committee (IOC) Session in Singapore in July 2005, beating off bids from candidate cities Paris, New York, Madrid and Moscow.

The heart of the London 2012 Games is a new Olympic Park in the Lea River Valley. But London, in contrast with recent Games, played down the role of iconic architecture, committing to build anew only when the long-term use of a permanent building could be justified with a viable business plan. To London 2012's credit, this approach has been stringently applied, though it has not been without its challenges, particularly in the case of the Olympic Stadium (see pp.78–85). When a future use could not be identified, temporary venues or permanent buildings expanded with temporary stands have been erected.

To make the most of historic London as a backdrop, Horse Guards Parade will host Beach Volleyball in 15,000 capacity temporary stands adjacent to St James's Park, while Greenwich Park will host equestrian events on a temporary platform. Existing venues, from west London's Wembley Stadium to the North Greenwich Arena (formerly the Millennium Dome), have been fully exploited to minimise the need for new buildings. ExCeL alone will house five temporary venues for seven different sports.

One of London 2012's most significant achievements has been to cut through the confusion that clouds the term 'sustainability' by quantifying environmental impacts. The very attempt to measure the Games' carbon footprint, no matter how imperfect a science that may be, must be recognised. This has led the London Organising Committee of the Olympic and Paralympic Games (LOCOG) to become the first Games Organising Committee to be certified British Standard 8901: Specification for Sustainability Management Systems for Events. This standard was inspired by the London 2012 bid and developed specifically to help the events industry operate in a more sustainable manner.

Priority themes were translated first into strategic objectives, then Key Performance Indicators and finally environmental targets with numerical metrics that were written into the planning

3 Location of Olympic Park in east London's Lower Lea River Valley. White lines indicate Transport for London Zones 1 and 2.

4 A strategic plan for enhancing east London's landscape infrastructure divides the area into six green grids. The Lea Valley corridor, location of the Olympic Park, occupies the north-west perimeter of the map.

3
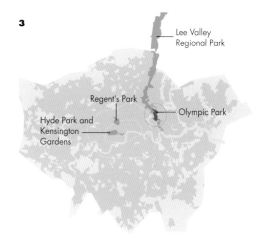

4 East London Green Grid, 2007

Chobham Academy   Olympic and Paralympic Village   Eton Manor   Velodrome   Westfield Stratford City   Basketball Arena

requirement for the new buildings. From engineers and architects, to contractors and their suppliers, these metrics have required every member of a project team to challenge conventional practice. Without a way to measure, it is impossible to assess success.

Not every ambition has been met, but there is much to applaud in London 2012's wide-ranging sustainability agenda. It was as much about training up local workers as it was about recyclable materials. At the peak of construction in 2011, more than 25 per cent of the workers on the Park lived in the Games' six east London Host Boroughs, well exceeding the 15 per cent target of the Olympic Delivery Authority (ODA). Every venue had an environmental manager on site, and a culture of environmental awareness was developed through simple messaging and regular presentations.

London's proactive approach to low carbon design was mirrored by an equally far-reaching accessibility strategy. Building on the UK's tradition of the Stoke Mandeville Games for war veterans in 1948, the premise of London 2012 is an inclusive Games with a new Olympic Park that is fully accessible to all. The Paralympic Games will be the

5 Aerial view of Olympic Park looking south with North Greenwich Arena and Canary Wharf in the distance.

Aquatics Centre · North Greenwich Arena · Lea River · Olympic Stadium · Primary Substation · Handball Arena · Energy Centre · Canary Wharf · International Broadcast Centre · Main Press Centre

biggest on record introducing the Games to a wider audience than ever before. A robust set of client's requirements, developed in consultation with technical experts and disability forums, summarised best practice from numerous sources and adapted it specifically for sports venues. An ambition to exceed mere compliance underpinned a desire to make the Games a welcoming and dignified experience for all. The message here is that an inclusive environment enhances everyone's experience, not just those with disabilities.

London's investment in the Games is about sustainability in its broadest sense. It is much more than an Olympic Park full of new sporting venues. It is about the creation of a sustainable urban quarter with an ecological park at its heart, where a quality public realm supports walking and cycling, and residential areas and community infrastructure are well located in relation to public transport. To be successful, the Park must be well frequented by local residents, in the best tradition of London's Royal Parks. But it must also reinterpret Britain's deep-seated horticultural traditions and adapt them to twenty-first-century environmental challenges. The UK's most influential urban thinkers, from Richard Rogers to Ricky Burdett, and many of its best architects and engineers have put their minds to this challenge.

During the early research for this book, it became immediately apparent that a cursory interview with the lead designer of each venue would barely scratch the surface of the many sustainability stories waiting to be told. I am most grateful to all the project architects, landscape architects, service and structural engineers, contractors' environmental managers and suppliers, who gave up their time to talk to me and to recount their tales from the frontline. Apologies in advance, though, to those I was not able to reach in the timescale and for the many more stories that could have made their way into this book.

Most importantly, London 2012's high-profile emphasis on sustainability has brought the subject to centre stage for all those directly involved with the Games programme: the International Olympic Committee, the UK construction industry, the planners of the Rio 2016 Games and east London itself. From the Greenway to the Olympic Park and beyond, nothing permanent was to be undertaken that could not be retained long term, and anything temporary had to be easily removable and reusable. This book suggests countless ways that the lessons of London 2012 can be adopted to design and build more responsibly. The Games themselves will broadcast environmental issues to a global audience, a first step towards the greater challenge of influencing people to adopt more sustainable lifestyles.

6 Olympic Park – Games Site Plan. 1. Velodrome 2. BMX Track 3. Olympic Stadium 4. Aquatics Centre 5. Olympic and Paralympic Village 6. Basketball Arena 7. Eton Manor 8. Hockey Centre 9. International Broadcast Centre 10. Handball Arena 11. Warm-up Venue 12. Water Polo Arena.

7 The steel tubes in the Olympic Stadium's circular compression truss were sourced on the surplus steel market, shortening the construction programme and reducing the amount of new steel fabricated for the project.

8 The Greenway. An underutilised footpath over the existing Northern Outfall Sewer has been upgraded as a pedestrian and cycling path along the Park's southern boundary.

9 London 2012 Legacy Masterplan (October 2011). London 2012 is the first Olympic and Paralympic Games to prepare a legacy masterplan prior to the Games. This map is indicative only.

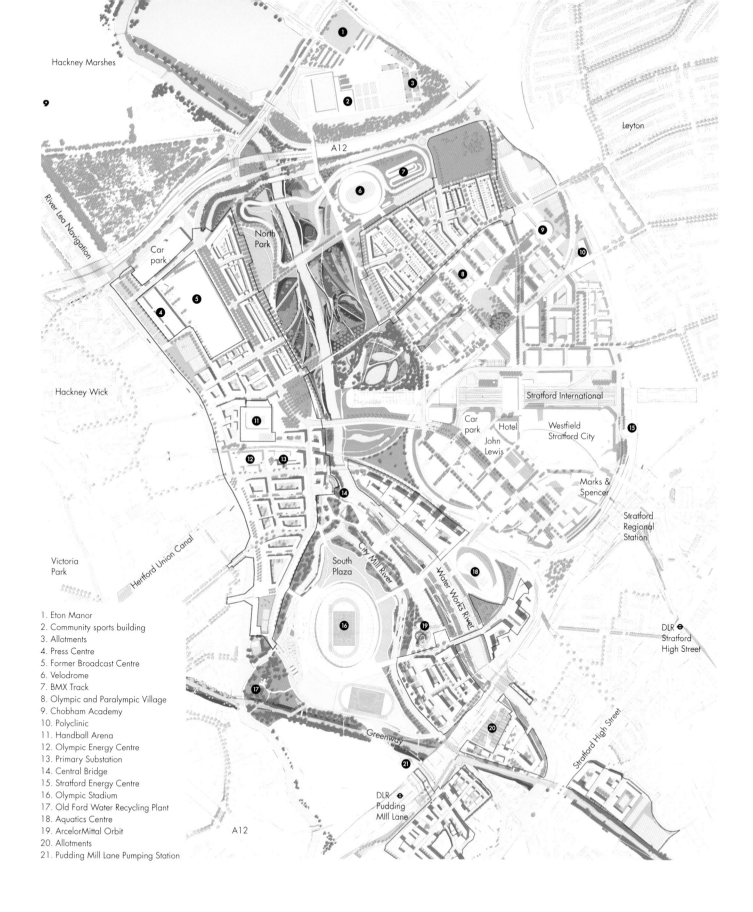

Hackney Marshes

9

Leyton

A12

North
Park

River Lea Navigation

Car
park

Stratford International

Hackney Wick

Car
park

Hotel

Westfield
Stratford City

John
Lewis

Marks &
Spencer

Stratford
Regional
Station

South
Plaza

City Mill River

Water Works River

Victoria
Park

Hertford Union Canal

DLR
Stratford
High Street

1. Eton Manor
2. Community sports building
3. Allotments
4. Press Centre
5. Former Broadcast Centre
6. Velodrome
7. BMX Track
8. Olympic and Paralympic Village
9. Chobham Academy
10. Polyclinic
11. Handball Arena
12. Olympic Energy Centre
13. Primary Substation
14. Central Bridge
15. Stratford Energy Centre
16. Olympic Stadium
17. Old Ford Water Recycling Plant
18. Aquatics Centre
19. ArcelorMittal Orbit
20. Allotments
21. Pudding Mill Lane Pumping Station

Greenway

Stratford High Street

DLR
Pudding
Mill Lane

A12

The Greenway

Beguiling use of materials reclaimed from the Olympic Park site and whimsical planting for biodiversity give the Greenway a wild quality reminiscent of the Lea Valley's post-industrial past. Linking West Ham station to the Olympic Park during the Games, the enhancement of this artery of east London's infrastructure is planned for legacy.

The Greenway, a linear park that runs along the southern boundary of the Olympic Park, opens this book because it is a microcosm of London 2012's achievement. Legacy, green infrastructure and connectivity, key aspects of London 2012's sustainability agenda, are embodied in this tiny project. Completed ahead of the Park, the Greenway – with its effusive planting – has proven a popular vantage point for viewing the construction of the Park.

Stretching from Wick Lane in Bow to the Thames at Beckton, the 7-kilometre-long Greenway runs along the elevated embankment of the Northern Outfall Sewer, one of London's most impressive Victorian engineering achievements. The sewerbank, as it was called for decades, serves as an informal footpath and cycleway. Thames Water maintains the sewer infrastructure and embankment, while the two boroughs it crosses are responsible for the path itself. Rechristened the Greenway in the 1990s after minor upgrading by the London Borough of Newham, the path suffered from disrepair and invasive planting when the proposal for the Games in east London was first mooted.

The newly established ODA seized the enhancement of the Greenway as an opportunity to involve small design practices in the Games. A design competition shortlisted five young practices for the project. North London office Adams & Sutherland were selected, largely because they valued the Greenway as it was and wanted to enhance what was already there. The Greenway was a test bed for many ideas and ways of working that were further developed in the Olympic Park.

Like the Olympic Park, the Greenway was conceived in terms of legacy from the outset. The ODA appointed CLM (a consortium specially formed for the Games and made up of CH2M Hill, Laing O'Rourke and Mace) Delivery Partner to help manage the delivery of quantifiable sustainability targets across the whole construction project. The longer term perspective influenced even small details of the Greenway design. Where a wider path is required to accommodate increased pedestrian flow to the Park for the duration of the Games, it is temporary, and its materials will be removed and reused after 2012. 'We were very keen on legacy,' explains Graeme Sutherland, of Adams & Sutherland. 'We weren't interested in connecting the edges for only six weeks. It was about catching the space and amplifying it in an area of loss and change. Our job was to make a great place and the mechanism for that was the temporary Games.'

10 Wayfinding is critical throughout the Olympic precinct because the new Park will link communities long separated by the Lea River Valley. New signage is an important feature of the Greenway.

View Tube

Stratford

Bow

 West Ham

The Greenway and Olympic Park are planned as connectors, linking two sides of the Lea Valley that for decades have been severed by waterways, and transport and utility infrastructure. The 2.3km stretch of Greenway upgraded for the Games includes seven bridges.

The Greenway is simultaneously a footpath and a cycleway, so the architects were challenged to specify surfaces that clearly distinguished these two uses. A precast pebble strip with an exposed aggregate surface divides the path in two, separating walkers and cyclists. Important for the public, this is essential for the physically or visually impaired. Responding to the ODA's requirement for recycled content in materials, the decorative aggregate specified for the Greenway surface incorporates recycled ceramics from old basins and toilets. The fill below the paving is reclaimed from the Olympic Park site.

The architects responded to the accessibility requirement for a resting place every 50m with a modern reinterpretation of the milestone: concrete blocks incised with cryptic altitude measurements referring to the sewer's gradual fall as it heads towards the Thames at Beckton.

11 The Greenway borders the southern perimeter of the Olympic Park and extends 7km to Beckton, as shown on this map. As part of a long-term strategic investment in pedestrian links and cycleways to the Olympic Park, upgrading of a 2.3km stretch of the Greenway was funded by the ODA in tandem with the construction of the Park.

━━ Greenway
• • • Greenway upgraded for the London 2012 Games
━━ Olympic Park Site Perimeter

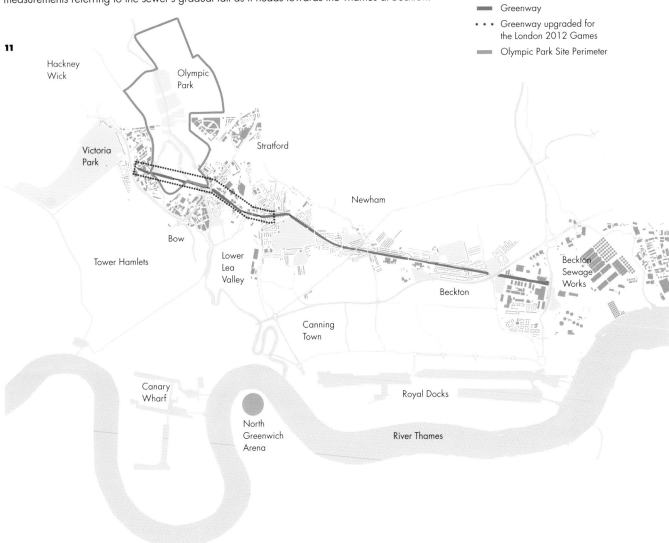

11

Hackney Wick

Olympic Park

Victoria Park

Stratford

Bow

Newham

Tower Hamlets

Lower Lea Valley

Beckton Sewage Works

Beckton

Canning Town

Canary Wharf

Royal Docks

North Greenwich Arena

River Thames

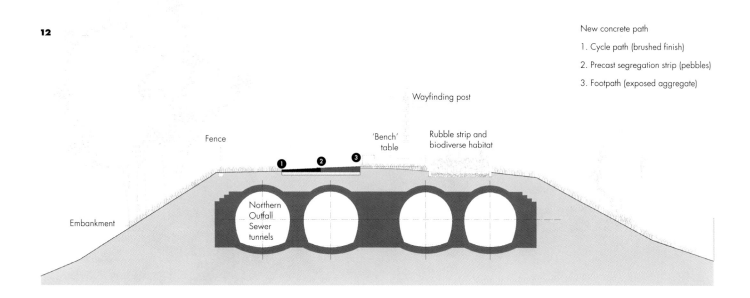

New concrete path

1. Cycle path (brushed finish)

2. Precast segregation strip (pebbles)

3. Footpath (exposed aggregate)

Wayfinding post

Fence

'Bench' table

Rubble strip and biodiverse habitat

Northern Outfall Sewer tunnels

Embankment

12 The Greenway, Section. Sited directly on top of London's Northern Outfall Sewer tunnels, the Greenway improvements include a new footpath and cycleway, signage and seating, fencing and extensive biodiverse planting.

'Using reclaimed materials is mainly about delight. There is no saving in terms of cost.'

GRAEME SUTHERLAND

Early design work on the Greenway occurred simultaneously with the dismantling of existing structures on the Olympic Park site. From pylons, lamp posts and bollards to cobbles, bricks and fill, the architects scoured stockpiled materials to see what they could reuse in the Greenway.

Strips of recycled cobbles punctuate the path in places, and manholes are laid in reclaimed granite setts. An attempt to reuse five of the 52 electricity pylons removed from around the Park as sculptural reminders of the past had to be abandoned due to liability issues.

As a piece of green infrastructure, the project ties into the East London Green Grid of open spaces. More than 20 rubble beds, a kind of brown roof on the ground, were constructed using railway ties and crushed roof tiles from the Olympic Park site. Planting was specifically selected to promote biodiversity.

The Greenway project highlights many themes and initiatives that will recur throughout this book. The emphasis on legacy and the importance of wayfinding in this poorly connected area of London will crop up again and again. A clear delineation between what should be permanent and what can be temporary pervades the Olympic and Paralympic project. Incentivised by the ODA's targets, careful scrutiny of material choices with precedence to reclaimed materials where practical and materials with minimal impact on the environment was of central concern to both designers writing specifications and contractors proposing

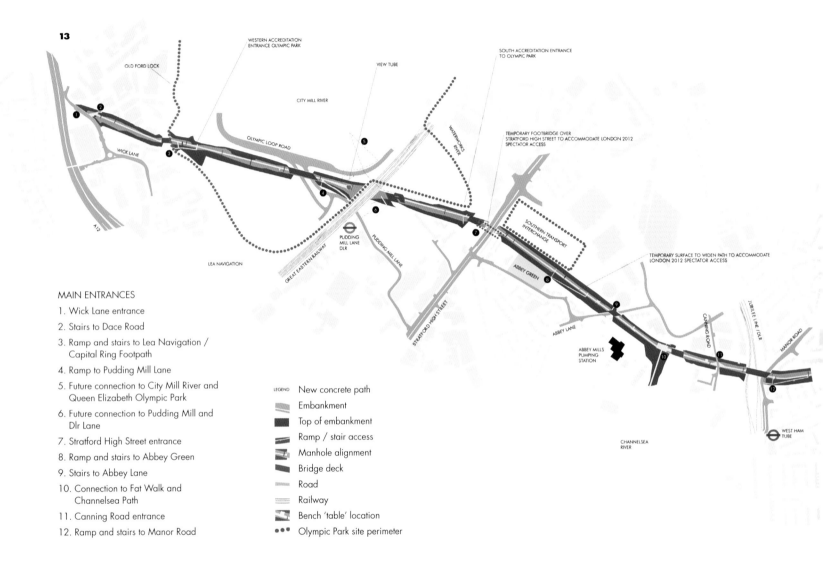

13

WESTERN ACCREDITATION
ENTRANCE OLYMPIC PARK

OLD FORD LOCK

VIEW TUBE

SOUTH ACCREDITATION ENTRANCE
TO OLYMPIC PARK

CITY MILL RIVER

WATERWORKS RIVER

TEMPORARY FOOTBRIDGE OVER
STRATFORD HIGH STREET TO ACCOMMODATE LONDON 2012
SPECTATOR ACCESS

OLYMPIC LOOP ROAD

WICK LANE

A12

GREAT EASTERN RAILWAY

PUDDING MILL LANE DLR

PUDDING MILL LANE

LEA NAVIGATION

SOUTHERN TRANSPORT INTERCHANGE

ABBEY GREEN

TEMPORARY SURFACE TO WIDEN PATH TO ACCOMMODATE
LONDON 2012 SPECTATOR ACCESS

STRATFORD HIGH STREET

ABBEY LANE

CANNING ROAD

JUBILEE LINE / DLR

MANOR ROAD

ABBEY MILLS PUMPING STATION

WEST HAM TUBE

CHANNELSEA RIVER

MAIN ENTRANCES

1. Wick Lane entrance
2. Stairs to Dace Road
3. Ramp and stairs to Lea Navigation /
   Capital Ring Footpath
4. Ramp to Pudding Mill Lane
5. Future connection to City Mill River and
   Queen Elizabeth Olympic Park
6. Future connection to Pudding Mill and
   Dlr Lane
7. Stratford High Street entrance
8. Ramp and stairs to Abbey Green
9. Stairs to Abbey Lane
10. Connection to Fat Walk and
    Channelsea Path
11. Canning Road entrance
12. Ramp and stairs to Manor Road

LEGEND   New concrete path
          Embankment
          Top of embankment
          Ramp / stair access
          Manhole alignment
          Bridge deck
          Road
          Railway
          Bench 'table' location
••• Olympic Park site perimeter

substitutions on all the projects. Thoughtful inclusive design, which addresses the needs of all users with appropriate finishes and resting places, is another constant theme.

The enhancement of the Greenway necessitated cooperation with numerous stakeholders, such as Thames Water, the London Borough of Newham, London Thames Gateway Development Corporation and the London Wildlife Trust. Going forward, coordination will be key. A maintenance plan is required that both preserves its wild side – it is a natural habitat for lizards, bats and kingfishers – and promotes activities that make it a destination as well as a path. Programmes that encourage local residents to walk and cycle, such as bike banks at local schools, should be facilitated. A similar approach will be essential for the future success of the Olympic Park.

13 Greenway site plan. The upgraded portion of the Greenway stretches from the A12 to West Ham underground station and includes several bridges over waterways, motorways and railways. West Ham station will be one of the recommended stations for spectators during the Games.

14 Wayfinding signposts are designed so that place names can easily be changed – an important consideration as new neighbourhoods are developed around the Park.

Hackney Wick

Lea Valley Walk 90yrds

Tube

Stratford

Bow

West Ham

15 Signage is playfully incorporated in the Greenway pavement.

16 This pavement detail is the key element of the Greenway design. A pebble strip delineates an exposed aggregate surface for pedestrians from a brushed concrete surface for cyclists.

17 Benches on the north-east side of Abbey Lane Bridge with existing utility pipe behind.

18 Rubble beds for biodiversity planting were created using roof tiles and railway ties from the Olympic Park.

19

KEY POINTS
- Design for legacy
- Linking across the valley
- Use of reclaimed and low impact materials
- Inclusive design
- Planting and rubble beds for biodiversity

19 Located on the Greenway, View Tube is made of recycled shipping containers and houses a café and education spaces. A partnership project supported by Leaside Regeneration, London Thames Gateway Development Corporation, the Olympic Delivery Authority and Thames Water, the View Tube and the Greenway have been popular viewpoints over the Olympic Park throughout its construction.

20 This modern interpretation of a milestone meets accessibility requirements for a resting place every 50m along the Greenway.

LEARNING FROM PAST GAMES

Before exploring in depth London 2012's own sustainability agenda, it is useful to set it in the context of the environmental achievements of previous Olympic and Paralympic Games. In 2000, Sydney was the first Host City to actively champion an environmentally responsible Games. Its Olympic Park, like London's, transformed a polluted industrial wasteland at Homebush Bay, 16km from the city's central business district, into a diverse landscape with a variety of ecosystems. A sophisticated water management strategy provided separate supplies for drinking and reclaimed water. Greenpeace developed environmental guidelines for Sydney's bid, even commissioning an architect to submit an anonymous design in one of the venue competitions. Renewable technologies were used at Sydney's Athletes' Village, now the suburb of Newington, where every house is partially powered by a rooftop photovoltaics (PV) array.

Immediately after the Games, lack of adequate pre-planning of legacy uses meant that Sydney's Olympic Park and sports venues were initially underused.

'Sydney was a great starting point; nobody has done better yet, though legacy took a long while to get properly fixed.'
LOCOG HEAD OF SUSTAINABILITY, DAVID STUBBS

Some observers noted that Sydney had not adequately exploited the city's existing venues before opting to build new venues at Homebush Bay. Sydney's 2030 masterplan for the area was launched only after the Games. Today, adaptation of the venues for ongoing uses has been relatively successful, but Sydney has been criticised for not tackling a long-term masterplan for Homebush Bay much earlier. Another important lesson from Sydney was the need for environmental targets and an auditing process to ensure that aspirations are delivered. Greenpeace performed a watchdog function for Sydney and scored the Games at 7 out of 10.

Pressure to meet the programme meant that Athens 2004 paid only lip service to sustainability. The need to ready transport infrastructure and venues for the Games meant that environmental and legacy concerns took a back seat. A WWF report rated the environmental component of the Athens Games at 0.77 out of 4. Athens scored well on improved transport infrastructure and for a general face-lift to the city (such as removal of advertisements from the main roads), but was marked down for its failure to protect fragile natural and cultural areas, a complete lack of low carbon building initiatives, and poor water and waste management. Of a total of 32 venues, 22 were purpose-built for the Games, and many have still not found long-term uses. A visit to Athens by the planners of London 2012 convinced them that any newly constructed permanent venue had to be justified by a clear legacy use. For London 2012, just six new permanent sporting venues have been built.

Beijing 2008 invested more than $17 billion in environmental projects in the run-up to the Games, according to the United Nations Environment Programme (UNEP), which advised the city on how to deliver a more sustainable Games. As part of its bid commitment, Beijing

21

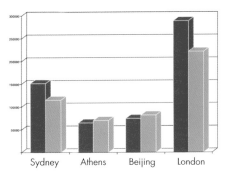

Sydney   Athens   Beijing   London

■ Temporary Seating
■ Overlay Area m²

22

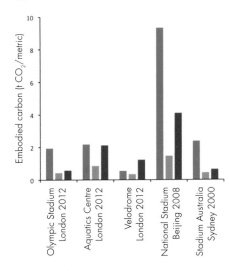

Embodied carbon (t CO₂/metric)

Olympic Stadium London 2012 · Aquatics Centre London 2012 · Velodrome London 2012 · National Stadium Beijing 2008 · Stadium Australia Sydney 2000

■ per roof area
■ per floor area
■ per seat

21 Chart comparing area of overlay and amount of temporary seating at London 2012 Olympic and Paralympic Games compared to three previous Games.

22 Comparison of embodied carbon for London 2012 Olympic Stadium, Aquatics Centre and Velodrome with stadia from Beijing 2008 and Sydney 2000. The low embodied carbon of London 2012's Olympic Stadium compared to the Beijing National Stadium is particularly striking.

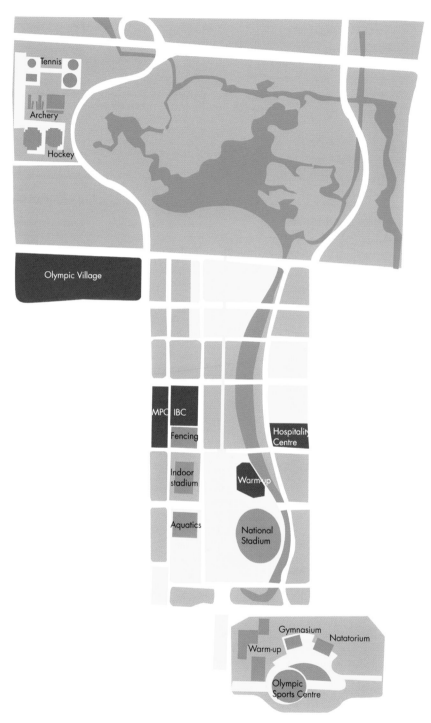

Tennis

Archery

Hockey

Olympic Village

MPC IBC

Fencing

Hospitality Centre

Indoor stadium

Warm-up

Aquatics

National Stadium

Gymnasium

Warm-up

Natatorium

Olympic Sports Centre

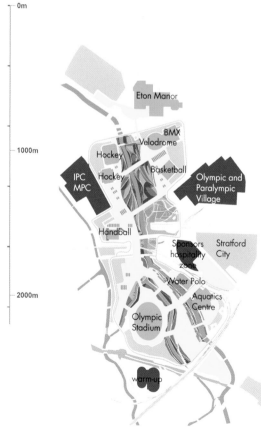

0m

Eton Manor

BMX

Velodrome

Hockey

IPC MPC

Hockey

Basketball

Olympic and Paralympic Village

1000m

Handball

Sponsors hospitality zone

Stratford City

Water Polo

Aquatics Centre

Olympic Stadium

2000m

warm-up

23 Diagrammatic plan comparing extent of Beijing 2008 and London 2012 Olympic Parks. London's Olympic Park is relatively compact with a minimum of permanent new venues, each carefully evaluated for its long-term viability.

set 20 ambitious environmental goals, aggressively tackling issues such as air pollution, transport, clean energy and sewage treatment. It is difficult to isolate and impossible to quantify the impact of the Games on Beijing's development, as many of the initiatives formed part of the normal development process for this growing metropolis. Beijing did, however, accelerate its investment programme to show the city at its best under the Olympic and Paralympic spotlight.

Located north of the historic city centre, Beijing's Olympic Park entailed the demolition of neighbourhoods to make way for the Games. Of its 37 venues, 14 were new, another 14 were renovated and nine were temporary. Numerous environmental initiatives were incorporated into the buildings, and a target called for 20 per cent of the electricity consumed in the venues to be supplied by renewables, but a comprehensive strategy was lacking. Herzog & de Meuron's Olympic Stadium, a steel-intensive structure with high embodied energy, also featured PVs. Such expensive renewables made a significant contribution to the agreed target, although energy-efficient passive design can reduce a building's overall carbon footprint more effectively.

China's emphasis on spectacular venues and impressing the world with the country's growing economic prowess sidelined any concern about how the Bird's Nest, the Water Cube or other venues might reduce their carbon footprint or be used after the Games.

24 Section comparing Populous's London 2012 Olympic Stadium (in black) with Herzog and de Meuron's Beijing National Stadium at Beijing 2008 (in red). The Meccano-like structure of the London Stadium uses approximately one quarter the amount of steel of the Beijing Stadium roof.

24

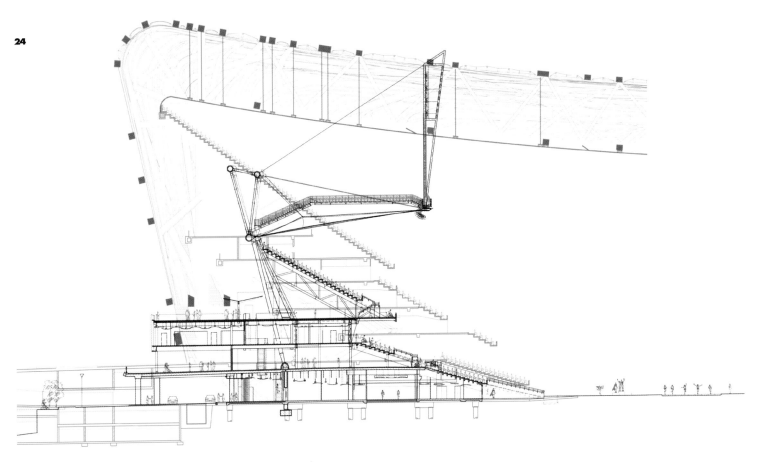

Like many other Olympic stadia, the stadium has struggled to find ongoing use beyond daily visits from curious tourists and occasional international sports events that partially fill its capacity of 80,000. In 2010, approximately half of the Water Cube was converted to a water park that caters to visitors and tourists. The iconic buildings are a draw, but Beijing's Olympic Park has yet to be fully integrated with the surrounding city.

By contrast, the choice of east London's Lea River Valley as the site for the Olympic Park was driven from the outset by economic regeneration. The success of Barcelona 1992 in restructuring and regenerating that city's waterfront offered a positive exemplar in this regard. The overriding lesson from Barcelona was the imperative to consider the Games and future uses simultaneously from the outset. London is the first Olympic and Paralympic Games where a legacy masterplan was prepared prior to winning the bid. Be it for transport, energy, infrastructure, the Park or the venues themselves, the show-stopping moment of summer 2012 was always viewed in the context of its long-term impact.

London is also unique in Olympic and Paralympic history in setting aside a specific 'transformation' budget and a timeframe for adapting the Olympic Park for community use after the Games. This is most evident in the proposed restructuring of the Olympic Park, where the bridges and concourses have been designed so that they can be dramatically reduced in size after the Games. In 2012, the ODA will turn the park over to the Olympic Park Legacy Company, which is bringing the remaining development sites to the market.

25 Aerial view of Sydney Olympic Park at Homebush Bay. The site of the Sydney 2000 Games was similar to that of London 2012 in that it occupied a contaminated site remote from the city centre.

ONE PLANET 2012

Current lifestyles in the UK require the resources of three planets: that is, if everyone in the world consumed energy, food and materials at the same rate as here, three planets would be required to sustain them. Members of various UK environmental NGOs, asked to contribute to London's bid in early 2004, sought an idea that would suffuse the entire bid and use the momentum of the Games to communicate a strong sustainability message. Concurrently the WWF-UK and London-based environmental charity BioRegional were developing the concept of One Planet Living, and the idea of a One Planet Olympics emerged from that early brainstorming. Not only was it an appealing and easily graspable concept, but also it provided a framework to transcend the minutiae of sustainability checklists.

The premise of One Planet Living is that we must live in a way that does not deplete planet Earth's resources. The idea behind a One Planet Olympic Games is to use the momentum of a high-profile event predicted to reach a potential audience of more than 4 billion televised viewers to raise awareness about more sustainable lifestyles. This starts by minimising the impact of the Games themselves and creating exemplar low carbon buildings and legacy communities.

26 An example of sustainable transport is this barge unloading steel rebar at the Aquatics Centre on the River Lea.

27 Chart of One Planet Olympics principles, 2004. This was developed into a strategy for both the Games and Legacy as part of the bid.

One Planet Living Principle	Strategy	Games	Legacy
Zero Carbon	Reducing carbon dioxide emissions by minimising building energy demand and supplying from zero/low-carbon and renewable sources	• Design and construction of London 2012 facilities based on maximising energy efficiency and use of low-carbon and local renewable energy sources • Basis for long-term sustainable energy infrastructure and management to be established	• Olympic and Paralympic Village capable of being energy self-sufficient • Distributed network of heating, cooling and power serving local communities • Energy-efficient sports venues
Zero Waste	Developing closed resource loops. Reducing the amounts of waste produced, then reclaiming, recycling and recovering	• No Games waste direct to landfill – all treated as a resource • Zero waste target a pivotal procurement driver • Closed-loop waste management at all venues • Public information campaign to promote high-quality front-of-house waste separation	• Zero waste policies extend across east London based on high recycling rates and residual waste converted to compost and renewable energy • Increased market for recycled products • Closed-loop waste management to be standard practice for major sports events
Sustainable Transport	Reducing the need to travel and providing sustainable alternatives to private car use	• All spectators travelling by public transport, walking or cycling to venues • Low/no-emission London 2012 vehicle fleet • Olympic Park Low Emission Zone • Carbon offset programme for international travel • Individualised travel plans as part of integrated ticketing process	• Increased connectivity across and between legacy development and neighbouring communities • Reduced car dependency • Car-free events policy adopted for other major events • Greater market for zero carbon transport
Local and Sustainable Materials	Materials chosen to give high performance in use with minimised impact in manufacture and delivery. Using local materials can benefit local economies and support traditional solutions	• Reclaimed, recycled and local construction materials used • Temporary buildings made for reuse elsewhere • Healthy materials used for construction and merchandise • Materials with low environmental impact used for merchandising • Robust Procurement and Management Systems implemented	• Reclaimed, recycled and local construction materials used during transformation into legacy mode • Training and job opportunities locally in (re) manufacturing • Local and sustainable materials supply chains maintained
Local and Sustainable Food	Supporting consumption of local, seasonal and organic produce, with reduced amount of animal protein and packaging	• Promotion of local, seasonal, healthy and organic produce • Promotion of links between healthy eating, sport and wellbeing • Partnerships established with key caterers, suppliers and sponsors • Composting of food waste as part of Zero Waste plan	• Increased markets for farmers in the region • Markets, catering and retail outlets supplying local and seasonal food • Composting facilities integrated into closed-loop food strategy
Sustainable Water	Reducing water demand with sustainable management of rain and waste water	• Olympic Park incorporating water recycling, rainwater harvesting and water-conserving appliances • Dual water quality supplies to new buildings • Recycled water used for irrigation or vehicle washing • Sewage and grey water fed into energy production	• Long-term sustainable water supply and management • Water-efficient homes and infrastructure • Lower Lea Valley self-sufficient in water • Ongoing management of waterways to provide amenity and wildlife habitat
Natural Habitats and Wildlife	Existing biodiversity conserved with opportunities taken to increase ecological value and access to nature	• Remediation of land and creation of large new urban park • Waterways rejuvenated to provide amenity and wildlife habitats • Olympic Biodiversity Action Plan implemented • Buildings and infrastructure designed to minimise ecological impact • Landscaping, planting and building design to increase biodiversity	• Net gain of ecologically valuable green space • Biodiversity an integral component of urban and park environment • People have greater local access to nature • Lea Valley 'green corridor' connected to River Thames
Culture and Heritage	Cultural heritage acknowledged and interpreted. Sense of place and identity engendered to contribute towards future heritage	• Development of Olympic Park to reflect local heritage and contemporary culture • Facilities to acknowledge, reflect and support diversity of local audience and global visitors	• Creation of a vibrant and diverse legacy community • Local and traditional industries revived to created employment and sense of identity • Ongoing development and management of legacy community to include public and stakeholder consultation
Equity and Fair Trade	Create a sense of community. Provide accessible, inclusive and affordable facilities and services	• Fully accessible facilities for all • Equity and Fair Trade an integral element of Procurement and Management Systems • Affordable ticketing and accommodation • Commitment to ethical business transactions	• High proportion of affordable housing • Mixed-use development to create sense of community • Opportunities for local employment and education • 'Green' business hub • Fairtrade community status achieved
Health and Happiness	Promote health and wellbeing. Establish long-term management and support strategies	• Extensive public and stakeholder consultation • Programme to promote the health benefits of sport and exercise • Healthy internal and external environments in the Olympic Park • Safe and secure facilities and environments provided • Facilities for worship and spiritual development	• Healthy internal environments in homes and other facilities • Improved air quality, visual amenity and soundscape • Community facilities to provide healthcare, vocational training and other support structures • Legacy community management and support structures to facilitate long-term sustainable living

While acknowledging that the premise of Olympic and Paralympic Games is inherently unsustainable because it entails a massive construction programme and countless international flights for participants and spectators for a few short weeks, the NGOs supporting the bid saw an opportunity to promote environmental awareness to audiences not normally reached by their campaigns. In 2004, WWF-UK and BioRegional signed a Memorandum of Understanding with London 2012 that resulted in *Towards a One Planet Olympics,* a seven-page document that set out the key themes of a sustainable Games. The concept gained mileage when favourably received by the IOC Evaluation Committee in 2004 after a presentation by Jonathon Porritt, the then Chair of the UK Sustainable Development Commission and WWF-UK's then Chief Executive, Robert Napier.

ONE PLANET LIVING PRINCIPLES

One Planet Living is based on a set of 10 principles that form a holistic approach to sustainability. WWF-UK and BioRegional translated each of the 10 principles, ranging from 'zero carbon' through to 'health and happiness', into strategies relevant to London 2012, both for the duration of the Games themselves and for the long term. This holistic approach made environmental sustainability an overarching theme of every aspect of the Games. The idea of a sustainable legacy was a key driver from the beginning, and the underlying aspiration was that hosting the Olympic and Paralympic Games could help the UK along its journey towards One Planet Living by fostering innovation and behavioural change.

For example, for the principle of local and sustainable materials, the strategy was that materials should be selected for high performance in use and minimum impact in manufacture and delivery. In terms of the Games, that translates into using reclaimed, recycled and local materials where possible, maximising temporary buildings that could be reused elsewhere and developing a robust procurement policy. In terms of legacy that means retaining the supply chains of sustainable materials established for the Games and fostering long-term training and job creation. The strength of *Towards a One Planet Olympics* was its pragmatic approach; it was more than an idealistic set of principles.

This early document called for sustainability targets against which delivery could be monitored over the life of the project. The lack of targets had been one of the criticisms of Beijing 2008 (Greenpeace China, 'Conclusions and Suggestions: Beyond 2008' in UNEP, *Beijing 2008 Olympic Games: An environmental review*) and particularly Sydney 2000's environmental achievements (Tony Fry, 'Sydney's Green Games?' in *Architecture Australia,* Sept/October 1997). As sustainability is a rapidly evolving field, the early strategists behind London 2012 were conscious that targets established in 2004 would need to be robust in order not to be completely superseded by 2013 when the Olympic Park would be turned over to community use. They needed to be simultaneously stretching, flexible and deliverable.

Another important early recommendation was a call for the establishment of an independent body that would monitor how London 2012 was delivering on its sustainability aspirations over the life of the project. This later led to the creation of the Commission for a Sustainable London 2012 (CSL), established in 2006. CSL provided an important interface with sustainability organisations and campaigners throughout the development process.

28 Seating in the Basketball Arena was leased from the hire market and adapted with a minimum of modifications so that it could easily be returned to the market after the Olympic and Paralympic Games.

29 The Basketball Arena is one of the largest temporary venues ever built for an Olympic and Paralympic Games. A premise of London 2012 from the outset was to maximise the use of temporary and existing venues.

30 (Overleaf) Because there was no confirmed legacy user for the Olympic Stadium at the time when the decision had to be taken to meet the programme, the ODA opted for a lightweight stadium that could easily be reduced in size for a smaller legacy seating capacity.

FROM SUSTAINABLE ASPIRATIONS TO TARGET METRICS

After the euphoria of winning the bid in July 2005, London 2012 had to find a way to deliver its sustainability aspirations. Sceptics had to be shown that London was serious about its commitments, and vocal minorities such as the cycling and allotment communities on the Olympic Park site had to be appeased. Sydney had demonstrated that an ecological Olympic Park could transform a contaminated site, but London wanted to go a step further and embed its sustainability agenda across its delivery structure for staging the Games and for east London's future regeneration.

This meant ensuring that sustainability had a seat at the top table on the Olympic Board so that it would not be conveniently dismissed when difficult decisions had to be made. It also meant determining where the biggest savings could be made and finding ways to measure and monitor progress. The challenge was to develop a sustainability policy that would underpin the work of all of London 2012's delivery organisations:

— LOCOG (established 2005) for the staging of the Games
— the ODA (established 2006) for construction of infrastructure and venues
— the OPLC (established 2009) for legacy.

The very fact of planning for legacy during bid stage and establishing the OPLC three years before the Games was in itself a significant departure from previous Games and indicative of a long-term commitment to sustainability in its broadest sense. Prior to the establishment of the OPLC in 2009, legacy was the responsibility of the ODA and LDA.

In 2006, London 2012 published its Sustainability Policy, a two-page document that laid out five 'overarching themes' to focus the Games' sustainability agenda: climate change, waste, biodiversity, inclusion and healthy living. The policy aimed high; on waste, its ambition was to serve as 'a catalyst for new waste management infrastructure in east London'. Healthy living addressed the thorny issue of behavioural change, seeing the Games 'as a springboard for inspiring people … to take up sport and develop active, healthy and sustainable lifestyles.' It also stressed the importance of legacy, aiming to 'transform the heart of east London'.

It could have all stopped with these lofty aspirations, but the Sustainability Policy also suggested specific steps to embed sustainability into day-to-day management. Partnerships with environmental charities, businesses, academia and community groups, a robust procurement policy and an independent auditing function for sustainability were all recommended at this stage. In 2007, London 2012 published the first edition of its Sustainability Plan which set out how sustainability would be delivered by LOCOG, the ODA and other key stakeholders. LOCOG commissioned a carbon footprint study and the ODA began to examine ways to set binding environmental targets for the construction programme. The number of policies and strategies proliferated.

The ODA's mission was the delivery of the infrastructure and venues on time and on budget, while at the same time maximising the opportunities for a sustainable legacy for the Games.

31 The Energy Centre houses the CCHP plant that powers district heating to the Olympic Park. The district heating reduces the operational carbon emissions of the Olympic Park and its venues by approximately 20 per cent compared to a conventional approach of individual plant rooms in each venue.

31

32

The ODA's Sustainable Development Strategy (SDS) is the key document that translated London 2012's five sustainability themes into objectives with binding targets. Based on a survey of best practice, the quantifiable targets (see pp. 39–41) had to be both deliverable in the short term and stretching to encourage innovation over the course of the project until 2012 when the Park and venues would be handed over to the OPLC. As noted in the Greenway project (p. 16), the ODA engaged CLM (composed of CH2M Hill, Laing O'Rourke and Mace) as their Delivery Partner, to act as project manager for design, procurement and construction supervision. Within CLM, each venue was assigned a sustainability team member responsible for monitoring the quantifiable sustainability targets. He or she worked collaboratively with the design teams constantly to identify opportunities for further innovation. This was managed under an Environment and Sustainability Management System (ESMS) certified to the International Standard for Environmental Management Systems (ISO 14001).

The ODA's commitment to quantifiable sustainability targets for the built infrastructure of the Games represents a major step forward for the Olympic Movement. Likewise, LOCOG's commissioning of a carbon footprint study meant that for the first time environmental impacts could be prioritised. Finally, the establishment of an environmental auditing process both through CLM and the Commission for a Sustainable London 2012 embedded a procedure for both championing the sustainability agenda and monitoring its progress.

Many of the key elements of the ODA's sustainability strategy were outlined in this important document, published in January 2007. The notion of permanent versus temporary was clearly espoused with a commitment to reduce the extent of the Olympic Park concourse by more than half so that it would be appropriately scaled for the future park. Designers were to submit documentation of how any temporary materials would be used or recycled after the Games. All permanent venues were to achieve the Building Research Establishment Environmental Assessment Methodology (BREEAM) Excellent rating, and a bespoke version of BREEAM was developed specifically for the 2012 Games sports venues.

An emphasis on carbon reduction highlighted a preoccupation with climate change that had not been a major concern in the planning of the Sydney 2000 Games a decade earlier. A 130m-high wind turbine at Eton Manor was proposed to contribute to the Olympic Park's renewable energy target, set at 20 per cent. Stretching numerical targets were established for reduction of CO^2 emissions in relation to the 2006 Part L Building Regulations, for recycled content in materials and for the use of recycled aggregate.

32 The Velodrome's predicted reduction in CO_2 emissions (over Part L 2006) is 32 per cent, far exceeding the ODA's 15 per cent target.

33

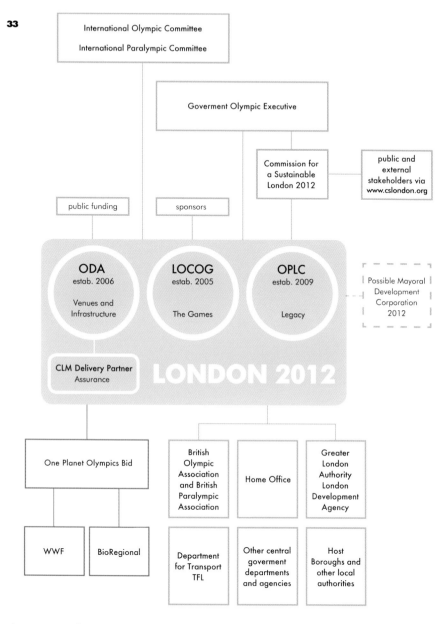

International Olympic Committee

International Paralympic Committee

Goverment Olympic Executive

Commission for a Sustainable London 2012

public and external stakeholders via www.cslondon.org

public funding

sponsors

ODA
estab. 2006

Venues and Infrastructure

LOCOG
estab. 2005

The Games

OPLC
estab. 2009

Legacy

Possible Mayoral Development Corporation 2012

CLM Delivery Partner
Assurance

LONDON 2012

One Planet Olympics Bid

WWF

BioRegional

British Olympic Association and British Paralympic Association

Home Office

Greater London Authority London Development Agency

Department for Transport TFL

Other central goverment departments and agencies

Host Boroughs and other local authorities

33 Organigram showing how sustainability was delivered across the entire London 2012 programme. LOCOG, the ODA and the OPLC each had separate lines of responsibility for delivering sustainability. The entire programme was reviewed by the Commission for a Sustainable London 2012 which made its findings public through a dedicated website.

34 (Overleaf) Halo lighting mast with wind turbine.

The ODA's performance targets take sustainable design to a new level. Although metrics alone do not guarantee sustainable buildings, they do encourage project teams to continuously scrutinise their decisions with a sustainability lens throughout the life of a project. All the project teams have been touched, and in many cases stretched, by the ODA's sustainability agenda, and this is certain to have a ripple effect through the industry. One contractor won a subsequent project for a building targeting BREEAM Outstanding based on their experience in the Olympic Park. Significant innovation resulted from this process; a notable example is the extensive trialling of new concrete mixes (see p.100). Only by tracking actual metrics can building performance be more carefully assessed and understood.

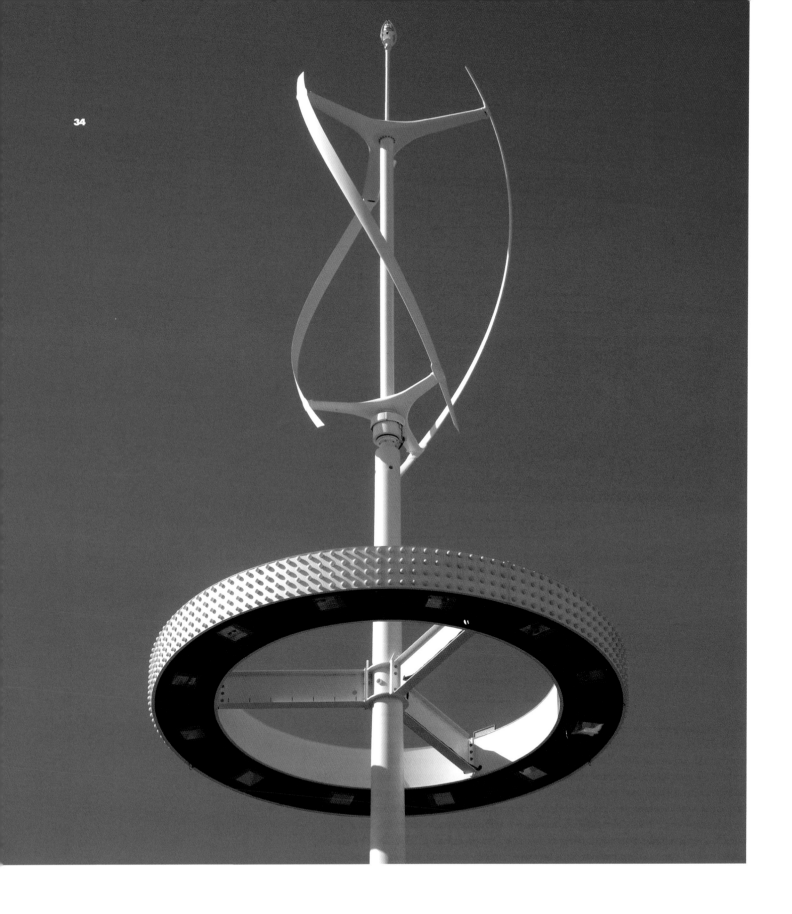

ODA, SUSTAINABLE DEVELOPMENT STRATEGY, JANUARY 2007		TARGETS
1. CARBON	*The ODA aspires to achieve a reduction in carbon emissions for the built environment of 50 per cent by 2013 [against 2006 Building Regulations]. This will be achieved by minimising demand and supplying energy using low carbon and renewable technologies.*	— Permanent venues should be 15 per cent more energy efficient than 2006 Part L Building Regulations. — Permanent venues should achieve BREEAM Excellent rating. — Olympic and Paralympic Village should be 25 per cent more energy efficient than 2006 Part L Building Regulations. — Olympic and Paralympic Village should achieve EcoHomes Excellent standard.* — Olympic Park to be supplied by Combined Cooling, Heat and Power (CCHP). — Renewable energy will meet 20 per cent of demand from 2013.
2. WATER	*The ODA seeks to reduce the demand for potable water by introducing water saving technologies, encouraging behavioural change and using alternative sources of non-potable water, such as rainwater and grey water.*	— Permanent venues and non-residential buildings should achieve a 40 per cent reduction in potable water demand, compared to current industry standards. — Residential buildings should achieve a target of 20 per cent reduction in potable water demand. — Rainwater harvesting and grey water recycling should be used where cost-effective.
3. WASTE	*The ODA seeks to design out waste and to maximise the reuse and recycling of material arising during demolition, remediation and construction.* When designing venues, materials selection and structure will be reviewed to minimise waste. This involves designing to standard sizes to avoid offcuts and maximising the use of secondary materials. Maximum manufacture of materials off site should be considered where appropriate.	— 90 per cent, by weight, of material arising through demolition works should be reused or recycled.
4. MATERIALS	*The ODA seeks to identify, source and use environmentally and socially responsible materials. This includes responsible sourcing, use of secondary materials, minimising embodied impacts and use of non-toxic materials.*	— 20 per cent secondary materials, as a percentage of materials value, in all permanent venues and the Olympic and Paralympic Village. — 25 per cent recycled aggregate, by weight, for all permanent venues and associated Olympic Park-wide infrastructure. — All timber to be from known legal sources with clear supply chain evidence. — Major building elements to achieve an area-weighted average rating of A or B in the Green Guide to Building Specification, third edition.

ODA, SUSTAINABLE DEVELOPMENT STRATEGY, JANUARY 2007		TARGETS
5. BIODIVERSITY AND ECOLOGY	*The ODA seeks to protect and enhance the biodiversity and ecology of the Lower Lea Valley and other venue locations.*	— Integrate habitat creation and landscape design into the design of venues. — Incorporate green or brown roofs where appropriate.
6. LAND, WATER, NOISE AND AIR	*The ODA seeks to optimise positive and minimise adverse impacts on land, water, noise and air quality.*	— Apply Sustainable Drainage Systems where geology and contamination allow. — Separate water and foul drainage systems to minimise water pollution and reduce flows to sewage treatment works. — Design park topography and infrastructure to accommodate one-in-100-year flood, 20 per cent increase in river flow and 6mm-per-year sea level rise due to climate change. — Minimise materials that include Volatile Organic Compounds (VOCs) and materials containing formaldehyde.
7. SUPPORTING COMMUNITIES	*The ODA seeks to create new, safe, mixed-use public space, housing and facilities appropriate to the demographics and character of the Lower Lea Valley and adaptable to future climates.*	— Protect and enhance 'sense of place' in the Olympic Park and surroundings. — Retain original structures where appropriate. — Olympic and Paralympic Village to meet Code for Sustainable Homes and Lifetime Homes standard. — Park, Village and permanent venues to meet Secured by Design standard. — Park and Village to meet Building for Life Standard Gold. — Venues and housing designed to adapt for future climate change, with ODA review during Stage C using London Climate Change Adaptation Checklist.
8. TRANSPORT AND MOBILITY	*The ODA seeks to prioritise walking, cycling and the use of public transport to and within the Olympic Park and venues and to maximise the environmental benefits of its transportation and logistics planning for materials during construction.*	— Transport at least 50 per cent of materials, by weight, to the Park by sustainable means during construction.

ODA, SUSTAINABLE DEVELOPMENT STRATEGY, JANUARY 2007		TARGETS
9. ACCESS	The ODA aims to model an excellent standard of accessibility that will act as an inspiration to others, and will be used as a benchmark by others.	— Design to gradients of 1:60 or less wherever possible. Maximum gradient to be 1:21.
10. EMPLOYMENT AND SKILLS	The ODA seeks to work with partners to create new employment and business opportunities, particularly for communities surrounding the Park, to facilitate the achievement of overall regeneration aspirations.	— Design legacy uses to maximise job creation.
11. HEALTH AND WELL-BEING	The ODA seeks to provide long-term benefits for the health and wellbeing of those constructing the Park and venues, and those who will use the facilities post-Games.	— Provide a Park and permanent leisure facilities for legacy that have lasting health and wellbeing benefits for the local communities and beyond.
12. INCLUSION	The ODA seeks to involve, communicate and consult effectively with stakeholders and the diverse communities surrounding the Olympic Park and venues.	— Create opportunities for community engagement in the design process. Provide a dedicated helpline, regular newsletter and visitor centre.

* The target of EcoHomes Excellent was subsequently changed to Code for Sustainable Homes Level 4.

A CARBON FOOTPRINT STUDY: MEASURING IMPACTS

A carbon footprint for an event or a building is its total impact on the greenhouse gases that contribute to global warming. London 2012 undertook a carbon footprint study to measure both the embodied and operational carbon of the Games and establish a reference footprint against which to identify carbon reduction opportunities. The report was intended to guide decision-making rather than simply report results, and it outlined a three-fold approach to carbon reduction: reduce energy consumption and materials, replace with more carbon-efficient alternatives and compensating unavoidable emissions by adopting a broad approach which focusses on knowledge sharing, partnership initiatives and behavioral change programmes.

Prepared by Oxford-based consultancy Best Foot Forward (BFF), the study was commissioned in March 2008 by LOCOG and supported by a specialist Carbon Technical Advisory Group that included the ODA and the London Development Agency (LDA). Published in March 2010, the study included any emissions that could be influenced by London 2012 and these were grouped into four categories: venues, transport infrastructure, operations and spectators. For venues and transport infrastructure, the reference footprint was based on material estimates for early designs and on bills of quantities for more advanced projects. Assumptions were tested by comparing carbon data for similar building types.

35 Research by Populous and Buro Happold highlighted the important role of embodied energy versus operational energy in the Olympic Stadium's overall carbon footprint due to its intermittent use. This was a strong argument in favour of a lightweight stadium design.

London 2012's carbon footprint was estimated at 3.4 million tonnes of carbon dioxide equivalents. Most is generated pre-Games: 50 per cent from venue construction and 17 per cent from transport infrastructure. Emissions controlled by the ODA and LOCOG comprise two-thirds of the Games emissions, with the lion's share (55 per cent) the responsibility of the ODA. The study demystified many preconceptions about Olympic and Paralympic Games, particularly the often cited role of spectator air travel. The operational and embodied energy in the venues, the transport infrastructure and the overlay for staging the Games are what London 2012 terms the 'big hitters'; hence, reductions in emissions associated with the construction activities could dramatically impact the overall carbon footprint of the Games.

Drilling down one more level, London 2012 identified the 'big hitters' within the venues as the Olympic Park's roads, bridges, utilities and public realm and the Olympic and Paralympic Village, which together comprise over 70 per cent of the venues' footprint, followed by the IBC/MPC complex and the Olympic Stadium. For each of the main venues, a carbon footprint was estimated based on a detailed breakdown of the quantities of different materials in the project using bills of quantities if available or by floor area. Embodied energy calculations were based on Bath University's Inventory of Carbon and Energy (ICE) V1.6 dataset, which was adapted for the Games. Emissions associated with transport to site by road of each material and on-site energy use were also calculated.

Understanding of the important role of embodied energy in the overall carbon footprint of a building has evolved significantly over the life of the London 2012 project. As the tightening of UK Building Regulations has caused a reduction in the operational energy of buildings, industry understanding of the importance of embodied energy has developed. One such example is in-house research by Populous on the relative proportion of operational and embodied energy in stadia. This research directly impacted the design of the Olympic Stadium and has had a knock-on effect on subsequent designs. With hindsight, one might say that the ODA should have required embodied carbon calculations for all the venues so that further reductions could be identified, but at the time that these targets were established, industry understanding of the important role of embodied carbon was just developing. Embodied energy calculations were required for all the temporary venues.

What is most important about the carbon footprinting exercise, like the ODA's sustainable construction targets, is that it quantifies, however imperfectly, different impacts. This mindset of measuring and reducing carbon permeated the Games programme and set the stage for the design of a low carbon Park and venues. Because of the timing of the study, its recommendations influenced the staging of the Games more than the design of the venues because the ODA had to proceed with commissioning the venues before the study was complete. The main lesson for future Games is that carbon footprinting should be undertaken as early as possible in tandem with masterplanning and venue design so that the results are available early enough to guide decision-making.

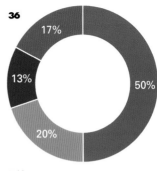

■ Venues
■ Spectators
■ Operations
■ Transport Infrastructure

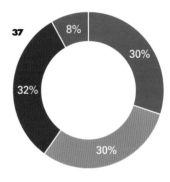

■ Concrete
■ Reinforcing steel
■ Structural steel
■ Other

36 Pie chart showing the distribution of carbon footprint between infrastructure and venues, operations and spectators.

37 Pie chart showing the breakdown of embodied carbon in primary construction materials used at the Olympic Park.

Chapter 2

Masterplanning

The masterplan for the Olympic Park precinct must be seen in light of London's overall urban development policy context. The UK Government's Urban Task Force (1999), chaired by Richard Rogers, had advocated that future development should reinforce London as a compact, connected city. Development of brownfield sites was to be prioritised over encroachment on the greenbelt, and expansion eastwards had been identified as London's future growth corridor.

'The notion of compact city and brownfield redevelopment was in the ether at the time.'
RICKY BURDETT, LONDON SCHOOL OF ECONOMICS

The masterplan for the Games could have taken many forms. Like Beijing and even Sydney, it could have been primarily about the architecture of the venues. Yet the scheme that was selected married ecology and green infrastructure with urban design and regeneration. This meant that protection and enhancement of the natural environment played a determining role in the location and design of new transport and utility infrastructure. Foreign Office Architects' visualisation of a sinuous landscape centred on the Lea Valley's waterways articulated the idea that a powerful landscape design would be at the heart of the Park.

Holistic thinking about landscape and green infrastructure permeated London 2012's approach to the Olympic Park site. Clearance and remediation of the site and the provision of new utilities and energy infrastructure were embedded from the outset with a strong environmental agenda.

THE BID MASTERPLAN

The masterplan for the Olympic precinct, which was initially drawn up in 2003–4 by the EDAW consortium (led by EDAW, now AECOM, and comprised of Buro Happold, Foreign Office Architects, HOK Sport, now Populous, and Allies & Morrison), predated the ODA culture of sustainability metrics. Yet it was sustainability in its broadest sense that underpinned the proposed regeneration of east London and won the Games for London in July 2005. The prevailing sentiment prior to the final bid was that Paris would win. This pervaded the design team, and there was a strong subtext that the masterplan had to make sense for London with or without the Games. According to the 2007 Index of Multiple Deprivation, three of the four boroughs adjoining the proposed Olympic Park – Hackney, Tower Hamlets, and Newham – are amongst the poorest of England's 354 local authorities, ranking second, third and sixth respectively. The Games offered a lever to change that, restoring both environmental equilibrium to a dilapidated post-industrial area and greater social equity to its residents.

1 (Previous page) Aerial view of Olympic Park site prior to redevelopment. Defining features of the site were the waterways, the railway lines and the dual carriageways. The Eastway Cycleway, site of the Velodrome, is clearly visible to the north of the site, as is the terraced housing of Leyton immediately to the east.

2 Early masterplan visualisation showing Olympic Park as part of a green spine stretching to the Thames. Initial proposals of the site for landbridges across major roads and railways were later modified.

2

Our vision for the Lea Valley

'Our proposal was about socio-economic change and environmental change. We were setting an agenda for what future city development would look like in the age of climate change and mitigation.'

JASON PRIOR, AECOM

The Lea Valley's river and canal network was the primary structuring element of the masterplan, which had the Olympic Park as its centrepiece. The Park was a connector that would link the two sides of the valley, bridging the waterways, railway lines and dual carriageways that had ruptured the urban fabric over the decades. It would provide recreational open space for the area, while better connectivity would improve access to employment opportunities and community facilities for local residents. The form and extent of the Park was determined by the topography and hydrological conditions that lay hidden below the post-industrial uses that occupied the site. The Park offered a means to alleviate tidal and fluvial flooding and enhance plant and wildlife habitats. It would also fill in a major missing link in the 26km spine of the Lee River Valley Regional Park, which runs from Hertfordshire to the River Thames.

Abutting the Park, the density and grain of development also responded to climate mitigation concerns. Residential density, initially envisioned primarily as four- to eight-storey blocks, was determined by walking distances to public transport and cycling distances to neighbourhood schools. The masterplan called for clearly defined built edges to the Park to create a sense of place and provide a density of occupation that would make the open space actively used. Proposed street layouts responded to both the fabric of historic street patterns and the discontinuities that had resulted from the overlay of transport and utility infrastructure. Different 'character areas' were identified to the east and west, which would be developed to enhance the particular conditions on either side of the Park.

3

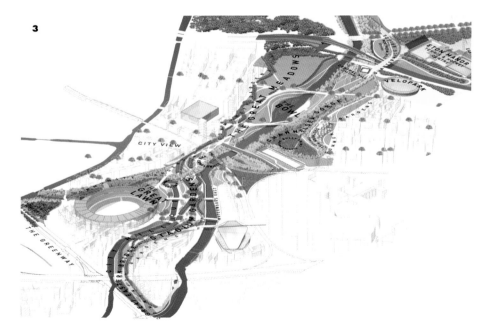

3 This early study for the Olympic Park, dating from 2004, illustrates the importance of ecological parameters – the waterways and the parkland – as drivers for the Park design.

4

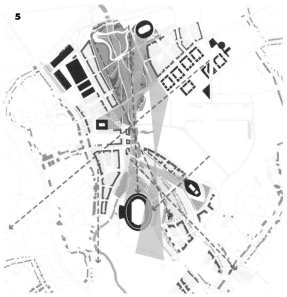

5

4 Masterplan evolution (2007) with sinuous landscape and iconic architectural venues. The early massing of the Olympic and Paralympic Village included a variety of building heights.

5 View corridors between the main venues and back towards the City informed the location of buildings and the axis of the Olympic and Paralympic Village.

TRANSPORT

Stratford's extensive transport infrastructure was the tipping point that made the Games in east London viable. A Games with high environmental aspirations had to be well served by public transport, a critical element in impacting behavioural change. One of London 2012's fundamental objectives was that 100 per cent of spectators should travel to the Olympic Park by public transport – or walking or cycling. The combination of Stratford International's direct connections to St Pancras and Europe with Stratford rail station's numerous suburban rail and underground lines made this part of London extremely well linked externally. The Docklands Light Railway (DLR) also connects Stratford to central London, Canary Wharf and London City Airport.

Approximately £6.5 billion has been invested in public transport by the ODA and its delivery partners, including central government, Network Rail and Transport for London. Permanent improvements and upgrades have been planned in relation to east London's projected future growth. An investment of over £125 million in Stratford Station has trebled its capacity, providing an accessible entrance, nine lifts and eight stairs, and new underpasses to Stratford Town Centre. A new platform for the Central Line allows carriage doors to open on both sides simultaneously. These upgrades are designed to accommodate the 500,000 passengers projected to use the station daily during the Games, but also to ease the station's morning rush hour, when passenger numbers are expected to double by 2016 (over 2008).

7 Diagrammatic map of public transport links to the Olympic Park via two adjacent rail stations, Stratford International (westbound to St Pancras International and eastbound to Europe) and Stratford Regional Station (three underground lines, Docklands Light Railway, London Overground and Network Rail).

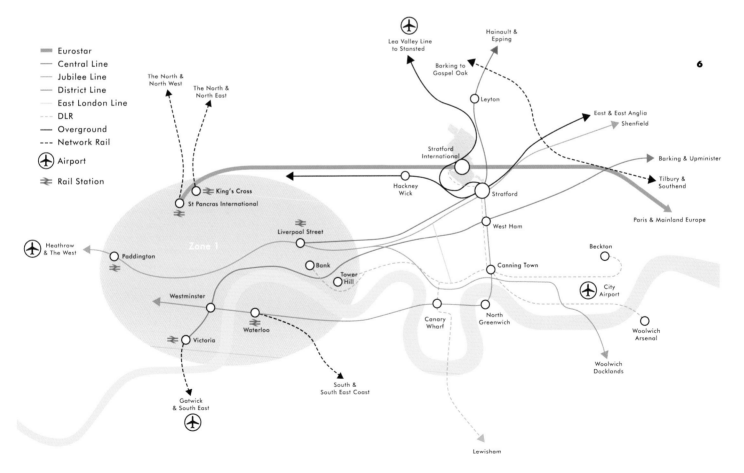

Upgrades to the DLR include an extension under the Thames to Woolwich Arsenal and an increase to three-car rather than two-car service across most of the network, increasing capacity by 50 per cent. Similarly on the North London Line, investment in new trains, signals and track means that four-car trains will replace three-car trains on much of the network. TfL-led investments that improve east London's transport for the long term include a 45 per cent increase in Jubilee Line capacity and extension of the East London Line with four new step-free stations and 20 new trains.

Some 300 additional diesel-electric buses will be added to the city's existing hybrid fleet of 56. Finally, over £10 million has been invested to upgrade cycling and walking paths to the Olympic Park. Paths have been widened and resurfaced, and access and connections improved. Over 100 such schemes are being delivered with local authority partners.

Before the 2012 Games bid, the market had already recognised the development potential of this enhanced transport, and a private consortium had submitted a planning application for Stratford City, a mixed-use development on a 30-hectare site assembled from former rail yards. When London won the bid, the Olympic and Stratford City masterplans were jointly revisited by the EDAW consortium for the Olympic Park and Fletcher Priest Architects for Stratford City. Infrastructure investment was coordinated, and the ODA was able to use the planning consent delivered through Stratford City to deliver housing that was already envisaged and required in the area. As a result, the Olympic and Paralympic Village, which was only 50 per cent within the Stratford City site at the time of the bid, was realigned to sit predominantly within the Stratford City masterplan.

7 Upgrades for the Games include trebling capacity based on long-term population projections for Stratford. The stairs of Stratford Regional Station (lower right) will lead spectators over the railway tracks to the Olympic Park during the Games.

DEMOLITION AND RECLAMATION

As soon as London won the bid, the focus of activity shifted to land acquisition, relocation of existing uses and cleaning up the site. Over 200 businesses with almost 5,000 employees had to be moved. A former landfill, a chemical works, a bus depot and a glue factory, not to mention a fridge mountain and piles of abandoned tyres, had left a patchwork of contamination across the site, the extent of which was unknown. The 2.5 square km site was criss-crossed by neglected waterways, rail lines and electricity pylons. Two 6km-long tunnels were dug under the site for the Park's new electricity cables so that the pylons could be removed.

The Orient Way project, which relocated a railway siding used to 'park' trains required only during peak hours from the concourse area between the future sites of the Olympic Stadium and Aquatics Centre to a site on the north-eastern perimeter of the Olympic Park, was an early demonstration of London 2012's commitment to sustainability. Over 4,000 tonnes of crushed concrete was salvaged, of which about 25 per cent was reused in the foundations of the new depot; the remainder was reused off site. All 2.9km of existing track were lifted and reused, including over 2,000 railway sleepers and more than 500 tonnes of steel rail. An on-site wind turbine supplies electricity for a new accommodation block for train drivers.

Meanwhile, the ODA had set a challenging target that 90 per cent by weight of demolition material from the site should be reused or recycled. This had important implications for the manner in which existing buildings could be demolished or dismantled: a process that was overseen by Atkins. If materials were to be reclaimed, they had to be carefully dismantled, inventoried and securely stockpiled. Overall a figure of 98.5 per cent was achieved, well exceeding the ODA's target. However, the majority of this was achieved through recycling rather than reuse – unsurprising given the urgency of the programme and the lack of established protocols for this type of reclamation work.

8

8 Reclaimed materials stockpiled on Olympic Park site in July 2008. Over 500 tonnes of yellow stock bricks and 170 tonnes of granite kerb stones were amongst the many reclaimed materials which were inventoried. Embodied carbon was calculated for all the materials.

9

BioRegional documented the dismantling process, working with demolition contractors and reclamation specialists to survey stockpiled materials and communicate to design teams what materials were available. While detailed reclamation audits were found to be very time-consuming, consultation with specialist reclamation contractors who were familiar with the market for reclaimed materials proved very worthwhile. Some opportunities for reuse were acknowledged to have been missed in the BioRegional report, but significant quantities of materials were also salvaged. These included yellow stock and Staffordshire blue bricks, granite kerbs and setts, roof tiles and heritage items including bollards, drainage gratings and signage. Clarity over who owns salvaged materials is critical as is good management of secure intermediate storage facilities.

The ODA required contractors to submit quotes for reclamation, but most were rejected due to inflated prices. BioRegional organised site visits for designers and workshops on designing with reclaimed materials. BioRegional's documentation of the demolition process on the Olympic Park concluded that because recycling is cheaper than reclamation or reuse, recycling was the fallback position for most contractors. An important lesson was that the only certain way to ensure reuse is to specify distinct targets for recycling, reclamation and reuse in both demolition and design contracts.

9 The West Ham Bus Depot facility amalgamates two bus depots relocated from the Olympic Park site. Designed early in the programme, sustainability was championed by client Transport for London. In addition to a sedum roof and wind turbine, the building's structure uses laminated timber arches.

SITE REMEDIATION

Now that eye-catching venues grace the Olympic Park, it is easy to overlook the magnitude of the soil cleansing operation undertaken by Morrison Construction and BAM Nuttall on the site. More than 1.4 million cubic metres of soil were treated, and 80 per cent of the excavated soil was reused on site, markedly above the 50 per cent industry standard. A 'soil hospital' employed industrial cleaning machines to remove contaminants such as oil, petrol and tar and toxic heavy metals including arsenic, lead and zinc from soil arising from pile excavations and utility trenches.

The combined drivers of the ODA sustainability agenda and the high cost of landfill led the ODA to employ four different remediation techniques to clean the soil so that the maximum amount could be retained on site. The majority of soil was simply washed, and the remainder was treated by complex sorting, chemical stabilisation or bioremediation. As soil was excavated, initial testing established the appropriate treatment method. Dedicated on-site laboratories enabled test results to be turned around quickly. Over 80,000 cubic metres of soil were treated by complex sorting, a technique not previously used in the UK on this scale, which involves running soil through a conveyor belt and removing harmful materials by hand. A large proportion of these materials were then sorted and recycled.

The wide range of end uses on the Olympic Park site added an additional level of complexity to the remediation process because each future land use had different levels of acceptable chemical criteria. The soil profile of each development site was modelled separately, with a total of 130 different conditions across the site.

10 The Park in 2007: sand, soil and aggregates were stockpiled in different mixes on the site of the future Velodrome to meet more than 130 conditions across the whole site.

11 Hand sorting at the Soil Hospital on the Olympic Park in 2007. The technique, not previously used on this scale in the UK, was used to remove and sort larger items.

12

Close collaboration with Atkins' geotechnical team enabled continual assessment of the precise makeup of the excavated materials to determine how they could be reused in enabling works on different construction sites across the Park. The majority of remediated soil was blended into one of four mixes with different combinations of sand and gravel that were then used as structural fill behind retaining walls, reinforced earth slopes and capping beneath roads. Over 10,000 cubic metres of concrete was crushed and used in gabion retaining walls across the Park.

12 View of soil washing machines at the Soil Hospital looking south along the River Lea with Canary Wharf in the distance, 2008. Over 1.4 million cubic metres of soil were remediated with over 80 per cent reused on site.

The Landscaping of the Olympic Park

Queen Elizabeth Olympic Park is London 2012's most potent environmental achievement, transforming a 2.5 square km contaminated brownfield site in Stratford. Its premise is to provide an exceptional setting for the Olympic Games and Paralympic Games, which can be easily adapted into a local urban park. Games and legacy were planned hand in hand from the outset, and extensive works to the Park will take place in 2012–13 to prepare it for community use, doubling the amount of Metropolitan Open Space from about 50ha during the Games to 102ha in legacy, just under the size of Kensington Gardens.

London sought to avoid the pitfalls of some previous Host Cities, where venues sit empty and oversized concourses become desolate wastelands. Munich's Olympic Park, which was created on the site of a former airfield on the city's edge for the 1972 Games, stands out as an exemplar of what is possible. Additions have been made to Munich's Olympiapark over the years, and it now serves as a multifunctional recreation area with sports venues and regular annual events that attract both residents and visitors.

The starting point for the Park design was the ecological corridor that connects 26km of the Lee Valley Regional Park in the north with canal networks and river corridors that link southwards to the Thames. The Park is intended as a 'green lung' for the east of London that will reduce the urban heat island effect. It will enhance the Lea Valley corridor as well as reintegrate an almost forgotten piece of the city with surrounding neighbourhoods. New roads, bridges, cycleways and paths will create physical links between previously disconnected neighbourhoods.

The Olympic Park is the largest new park since Victorian times and builds on Britain's long tradition of urban landscaping. Yet it represents a new departure in British park design because it aims to provide much more than an amenity landscape of grass and trees with ornamental planting. Its driving force is restoration of the site's natural ecological balance.

EVOLUTION OF THE PARK DESIGN

At bid stage, the London 2012 Olympic Park was presented as a series of sporting venues dominating the green space. The language of the bid spoke to One Planet Living's 10 principles of sustainability developed by BioRegional and WWF-UK, but the predominant impression of the bid masterplan is an agglomeration of sporting venues rather than a park. The notion of temporary and flexible venues that could be reduced in size post-Games was suggested, but the idea was not developed.

ENVIRONMENTAL PROFILE

Biodiversity created: 45ha of new habitat; 675 bird and bat boxes

Soil cleaned and reused on site: 1.4 million cubic metres, 80% reused

Approximately 67% of materials has been moved to the Park by sustainable transport

MATERIALS

Primary hardscape materials: cold foam asphalt

Recycled materials: crushed concrete in gabion walls, SUDS drainage blocks of recycled plastic

Innovative materials and products: Vegecol binder for cold foam asphalt, halo lighting masts with micro wind turbines

13 Aerial view of the River Lea in the north of the Park. The widened river has been planted with reed beds and the banks reinforced with wildflower turf. Tiered timber seating overlooks the river.

Initially masterplanned by EDAW (now AECOM) with Allies & Morrison, the Park design provides a more urban setting in the south, with paved areas to host artistic and cultural community events, and a more natural greener landscape in the north. In 2008 once the strategic drivers of infrastructure and masterplanning were in place, the ODA turned its attention to creating a characterful Park and commissioned LDA Design in association with American landscape practice Hargreaves Associates to further develop the project. Hargreaves Associates, designers of Sydney's Olympic Park, are particularly known for reclamation work with brownfield sites, such as the St Louis, Missouri waterfront and San Francisco's Crissy Field.

After comparative studies with Sydney and crowd modelling simulations, the LDA/Hargreaves team made three major changes: reducing the size of the pedestrian concourses by almost 20 per cent, opening out the slope of the riverbanks to make the waterways more visible and accessible, and modulating the landform to raise the Park level above the concourse and create a sense of landscape enclosure. Using a physical model to shape the Park topography, the new design team framed views of venues, introduced a sequence of vistas leading to the northern Park and used elevation to enclose the northern end of the Park where it abuts the busy A12. Throughout the changes to the topography, an overriding objective was to reuse all excavated material within the Park to avoid transporting materials off site. Ornamental gardens that showcase British plant collecting and horticulture form part of the displays on the main concourse, but the bulk of the Park was envisioned as a carefully designed balance of different habitats.

WATER

The movement and treatment of water was a fundamental determinant of the Olympic Park's design. The wish was to create an absorbent landscape that could resist flooding and at the same time include wetlands that slow water absorption and clean rainwater run-off. Key objectives were to resolve longstanding sewage effluent, which flowed up into the site from the Thames on certain high tides, and to mitigate potential flooding in communities to the north. To this end, the Waterworks River was widened by 8m alongside the Aquatics Centre and the Water Polo Arena – serving the dual purpose of creating a more prominent water feature at the heart of the Park and increasing its conveyance capacity. A Wetland Bowl in the north park also provides additional storage capacity during flood events.

The Lea River and its associated canal network comprise a 8.35km loop of waterways in and around the Olympic Park, which divide into the Bow Back Rivers south of the site. An early component of the enabling works, completed in 2009, was the £20 million construction of Three Mills Lock on the Lower Lea River, which reduces tidal fluctuation and creates freshwater conditions within the Park. In a derelict state for the last 40 years, both the river and canal network required dredging to restore their navigability.

The London 2012 Biodiversity Action Plan submitted as part of the planning application called for the creation of 0.27ha of new backwater along the River Lea with at least one continuous vegetated bank to provide an ecological corridor, habitat structure and hydraulic connectivity with the floodplain. As part of the design, 2.3km of new soft riverbank has been created. Further work includes a detailed programme of invasive species control, bank remodelling, towpath construction and planting of aquatic vegetation.

14 Non-potable water network. Water from the Old Ford Water Recycling Plant is distributed through the Park for irrigation, reaching as far as the hockey pitches at Eton Manor north of the A12.

In the north of the Park, the riverside footpaths are set at 4m Above Ordnance Datum (AOD), while the River Lea normally fluctuates between 2.3m and 2.7m AOD. It is predicted that the river will overtop the footpaths four to seven times a year when heavy rainfall coincides with high tides in the River Thames. Soft planting areas behind footpaths are designed to temporarily store excess water during these seasonal inundations. Additional flood management is achieved through biological swales with checkdams that slow surface water as it flows back into the river. A culvert was extended to divert floodwater from a railway line east of the Park, reducing flood risk to 4,000 nearby properties.

Due to the ground contamination and the need to get flood waters down the catchment rapidly, the flood concept was to promote the flow of surface run-off to the waterways. Through the use of porous paving and SuDS, the concourse and towpaths are designed to be flood-resistant, and the aquatic planting is designed for flooding through the introduction of a variety of wetland species. Wetland bowls and frog ponds are designed to hold back water and release it slowly into the river after it has been cleansed through a natural process. Use of SuDS on this scale is unprecedented in the UK.

OLD FORD WATER RECYCLING PLANT

A key objective of London 2012's water strategy, as set out in the Sustainable Development Strategy, is a 40 per cent reduction of potable water use for all the permanent non-residential venues compared to industry standard. About half of this target is met through measures such as specification of water-saving sanitaryware and efficient irrigation methods. The Velodrome and the Handball Arena also contribute to the reduction of water use through rainwater harvesting, and the Aquatics Centre with filter backwash recycling.

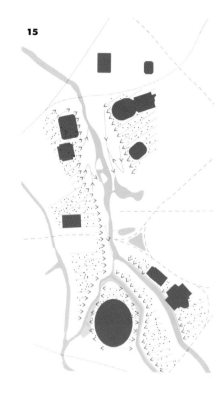

15 A study of Water Edge Treatments on the Olympic Park site. The waterways were one of the main drivers for the Park design.

16 Visualisation of Old Ford Water Recycling Plant. Located in a woodland area south-west of the Olympic Stadium, the plant uses an innovative technology to process recycled water from the adjacent Northern Outfall Sewer for reuse on the Olympic Park site.

Various approaches to site-wide water savings, such as drawing water from the aquifer, greywater and rainwater harvesting, were all considered. The cost of and logistics of storage requirements for rainwater or greywater on the scale required was prohibitive. Thames Water emerged as a potential funding partner for a water recycling treatment plant on the Olympic Park site as part of a research programme associated with its new desalination plant in Beckton, east London, completed in 2010. The ODA opted for black water recycling as the most sustainable option because it does not draw on a new water source.

Used for the first time in the UK on a municipal scale, the water recycling plant employs the same technology as the installation at BedZed in Sutton in south-west London. Located at the south-west corner of the Olympic Park, it will treat water from London's Northern Outfall Sewer, which runs adjacent to the Olympic Park, and result in approximately 40 per cent reduction in drinking water use. To achieve the required gravity feed from the sewer, the optimal site for the plant was located within a small nature conservation area just south of the Olympic Stadium. Waste water is passed through membrane bioreactors and filters that remove undesirable elements. Water will be treated to a standard suitable for non-potable uses, such as landscape irrigation, toilet flushing in the Stadium, Main Press Centre and Eton Manor, cooling the Energy Centre's combined heat and power plant, and topping up the Velodrome and Handball Arena rainwater systems. A seven-year research programme with Thames Water will monitor the functioning and costs of the plant. The timber-clad building was designed to be in keeping with its woodland setting and incorporates gabion walls and a living roof to enhance biodiversity (see pp. 176–179).

CONNECTIVITY
In addition to the waterways, the other driving force in the Park design has been creating pedestrian, cycle and vehicular links across the site to connect the Park to surrounding

17 Wet woodland in the south of the Park with Energy Centre beyond. The banks have been regraded and invasive species removed. New native species include reed, iris, willow and alder.

18 Visualisation of Central Bridge in legacy. Once the temporary decks are removed, the thin profile of the bridge is intended to disappear into the landscape.

19 Central Bridge, detail of temporary deck. The bridge has a multi-coloured temporary deck that infills the zed-form of the permanent bridge to accommodate spectators during the Games.

neighbourhoods. The notion of connectivity pervades the physical planning of the Park. In terms of east–west connections across the Lea Valley, the Olympic Park will actually tie together four London boroughs: Hackney and Tower Hamlets to the west and Waltham Forest and Newham to the east.

To this end, the Park design includes more than 30 new bridges, which cross the site's numerous waterways, rail lines and roads. Several bridges have temporary decks that will be removed after the Games. A typical bridge design developed by Allies & Morrison and Arup has been adapted Park-wide. An important principle of the bridge design is visual integration with the landscape to enhance the continuity of the natural landscape through the Park. A gabion wall detail that incorporates crushed concrete from demolished buildings on the site was adopted throughout the site for bridge abutments and wing walls.

One of the bridges in the north of the Park incorporates an art installation by artist Martin Richman that uses recycled glass and slag, a glass waste byproduct. Entitled *One Whirl*, the installation uses two different colours of recycled glass to create a swirling pattern in the deck surface. Blocks of slag, which will be illuminated at night, are used in the gabion baskets that form the structure of the bridge. This imaginative use of slag combines art, design, engineering and sustainability.

CENTRAL BRIDGE
A key bridge linking the Olympic Stadium and the Aquatics Centre to the north Park, was the subject of an international design competition that received 46 entries. The winning entry by Irish practice Heneghan Peng Architects with Adams Kara Taylor Engineers is made up of two footbridges connected by a diagonal 'Z' blade that spans the old River Lea and Carpenters Lock, a 1930s lock that will be restored by British Waterways.

20 Construction photograph of Central Bridge. Gabion walls make use of crushed concrete from the Olympic Park site and provide crevices for flora and fauna. The polished stainless steel underside of the bridge is intended to reflect as much light as possible into the towpath.

21 Transformation of typical bridge for legacy. Numerous bridges in the Park have been designed with a temporary section so that they can be reduced in width after the Olympic and Paralympic Games.

During the Games, a temporary deck will sit between the two permanent footbridges to create a 55m-wide bridge capable of accommodating large numbers of spectators.

The final bridge form was conceived to be as light as possible to allow the landscape and natural light to take precedence over the bridge's built form. It was conceived to be easily adapted after the Games with minimal construction. The underside of the bridge's steel structure is clad in mirror-finish stainless steel to reflect as much light as possible below the bridge for the benefit of pedestrians. The cladding panels were standardised so that they could be prefabricated from flat sheets, minimising the requirement for specially machined modules. Lighting is a major aspect of the bridge design and LED lighting is used throughout.

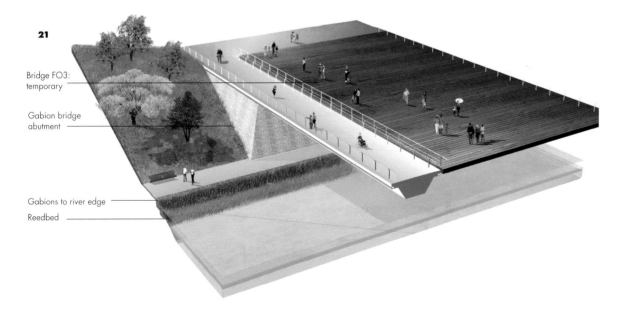

Bridge FO3: temporary

Gabion bridge abutment

Gabions to river edge

Reedbed

PLANTING

The Olympic Park represents a new chapter for landscape design in the UK because it is an ecological rather than an amenity landscape. First pioneered by J.P. Thijsse in the Netherlands, with one of the more notable examples being Jac. P. Thijssepark in Amstelveen, this approach to landscape design combines aesthetic and environmental concerns. Planting is viewed as part of a dynamic landscape, designed to look beautiful, control water movement and enhance biodiversity.

The London 2012 Biodiversity Action Plan requires 45ha of designated habitats and local sites of nature conservation throughout the Olympic Park. Topsoil and subsoil mixes specifically tailored to the different habitats have been introduced where necessary. Almost 700 wildlife installations are incorporated into the landscape. Wildflower meadows planted with annuals to peak during the Olympic and Paralympic Games will be replaced with perennial meadows. The wet woodland habitat created in the Park will greatly increase the amount of this very rare habitat in the UK. Drought-resistant species of trees and plants have been selected in anticipation of higher temperatures and reduced water conditions due to climate change.

22 Herbaceous planting in the Southern Hemisphere 2012 Gardens is concentrated along the main concourse near the Aquatics Centre.

23

ACCESSIBILITY
Access for disabled people has been considered throughout the Park design, with particular attention given to bridges. No slope in the Park is greater than 1:21 and where possible achieves 1:60. Bespoke benches with armrests at the requisite height are located at 50m intervals. The concourse surface and patterning has been approved for the visually impaired.

BENCHES AND LIGHTING
All timber specified for benches in the Park was subjected to a rigorous assessment of its chain of custody. The stamp alone of FSC and PEFC certification was not considered sufficient. The ODA required an audit trail documenting every step – provenance, milling, shipping and manufacture – to ensure that no uncertified timber was mixed with sustainably sourced material.

Two types of lighting masts are used in the Olympic Park. Along the main concourse near the Olympic Stadium, outdoor LED lighting will have one of its first applications in the UK. Seven halo fittings on 30m-high masts topped with wind turbines were developed by Philips especially for London 2012. Throughout the rest of the Park, a single head fitting with a PV panel is standard.

23 View of the north of the Park. The widened and replanted banks of the Lea River are designed to be flood absorbent.

24 Section through Waterworks River. An important design change at the end of Stage C was to regrade the riverbank to improve the visual and physical connection between the concourse and the river.

24 Revised Waterworks
Riverbank Proposal

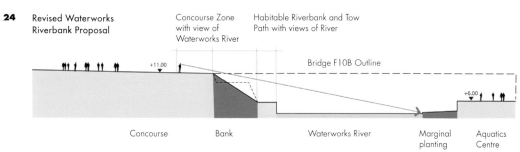

Concourse Zone
with view of
Waterworks River

Habitable Riverbank and Tow
Path with views of River

Bridge F10B Outline

+11.00

+6.00

Concourse   Bank   Waterworks River   Marginal   Aquatics
planting   Centre

Existing Stage C Section

**Revised Waterworks
Riverbank Proposal**

Concourse Zone
with view of
Waterworks River

Habitable Riverbank and Tow
Path with views of River

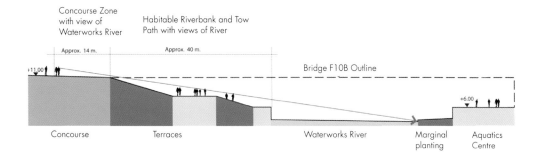

Approx. 14 m.   Approx. 40 m.

+11.00

Bridge F10B Outline

+6.00

Concourse   Terraces   Waterworks River   Marginal   Aquatics
planting   Centre

Proposed Adjustment to
Stage C Section

25 Halo lighting masts with integrated wind
turbines overlook elegantly curved concrete
seating on the Olympic Park. Because the Park
design calls for over 2km of seating the choice
of material was carefully considered. A life-
cycle analysis approach was used, weighing
criteria such as carbon footprint, waste and
toxicity against conventional construction
criteria including durability and cost.

TRANSFORMATION

London 2012 is the first Olympic and Paralympic Games where substantial funding was
earmarked ahead of the Games to adapt the Olympic Park and venues for future community
use. Many roads, bridges and concourses are to be transformed post-Games. Connections to
adjacent neighbourhoods, referred to by the ODA design team as 'stitches', will be opened
and planted during the transformation phase. The nature of the roads will be redesigned to
resemble urban boulevards such as The Mall, rather than loop roads used to service the Park
during the Games.

FUTURE MANAGEMENT AND MAINTENANCE

A final aspect of the Olympic Park that will be critical to its success will be the funding and
programming of legacy activities. Considerable forward planning and budgeting of legacy
activities was undertaken during the design phase to anticipate the Park's future needs. The
ODA recommended the establishment of a trust based on New York City's Battery Park
City to ensure the Park's future by isolating its management from political vicissitudes. The
Olympic Park Legacy Company (OPLC)'s current plan proposes a Park-wide management
and maintenance plan operated by the office of the Mayor of London.

KEY POINTS

Ecological dynamic landscape
Biodiversity
Water recycling treatment
Transformation for community use
Importance of legacy funding and management

26 North Park with Velodrome beyond. The banks of the River Lea have been regraded to make the river the central feature of the north Park. Footpaths line its banks and the river is visible from the Park concourse.

OLYMPIC PARK ENERGY STRATEGY: LEAN, MEAN AND GREEN

The energy strategy for the Olympic Park must be seen in the context of the drivers that were prevalent during the early infrastructure planning for the Park in 2006. *The Mayor's Energy Strategy: Green light to clean power* (2004) had established London's energy hierarchy as lean, green and clean: reduce demand, use renewable energy and supply energy efficiently through Combined Cooling Heat and Power (CCHP) and local energy generation. Subsequently specific targets for renewable energy generation were established, initially at 10 per cent and then increased to 20 per cent as a planning requirement, reflecting the changes in the London Plan.

THE ODA'S APPROACH
In line with this thinking, the ODA developed its own strategy as lean, mean and green. Reduced demand was its starting point. Because there was a strong presumption in favour of community heating while the planning applications for the Olympic Park and Stratford City were being developed, the ODA prioritised district heating as its second strategy to take advantage of economies of scale and minimise heat loss in transmission. Renewable energy, viewed as more costly, was third. The sum of these three approaches was to achieve a 50 per cent reduction in carbon emissions (against 2006 Building Regulations) for the London 2012 development programme.

It is worth pointing out that this was the early days of the Merton rule – initially adopted in 2003 – which made 10 per cent renewables a planning requirement. Very few precedents for district heating (Woking and Southampton are notable exceptions) existed in the UK. The cleared 2.5 square kilometre site of the Olympic Park, with its mix of venues, offered an opportunity to test the market for private investment in district heating. By this point, Westfield (see p. 200) was developing its Stratford City project and was already exploring district heating options. The even greater economies of scale offered by looking at energy provision for the Olympic Park together with Stratford City seemed a logical approach.

The fixed July 2012 date for the Games and the imperative to minimise risk meant that only proven technologies could be considered for the Olympic Park. The diversity of building types with different heating demand profiles – sports venues, the Aquatics Centre with its constant heating demand for the pools, Westfield shopping centre and the Olympic and Paralympic Village housing – made CCHP particularly attractive. A flexible energy infrastructure that could expand to meet increased development after the Games was essential. Finally, the market had to be tested to identify an approach that would attract private sector investment.

ENERGY TARGETS
The ODA established its energy targets in relation to permanent buildings only: 15 per cent through energy efficiency, 20 per cent through a combined heating and cooling network and an additional 20 per cent from on-site renewables.

A target of reducing demand by 15 per cent over Part L 2006 was written into the design briefs for the permanent venues. At the time this 15 per cent target was set, 2006 Part L

27 The CCHP-fired district heating system is the primary element of the Olympic Park's energy strategy. Centralised generation of power in the Olympic Park Energy Centre is much more efficient than locating plant rooms in every venue.

28 London Thames Gateway Heat Networks (LTGHN). Map showing district heating system at Olympic Park linked to Barking Power Station.

29 Bespoke lighting masts with small wind turbines were supplied for the main concourse.

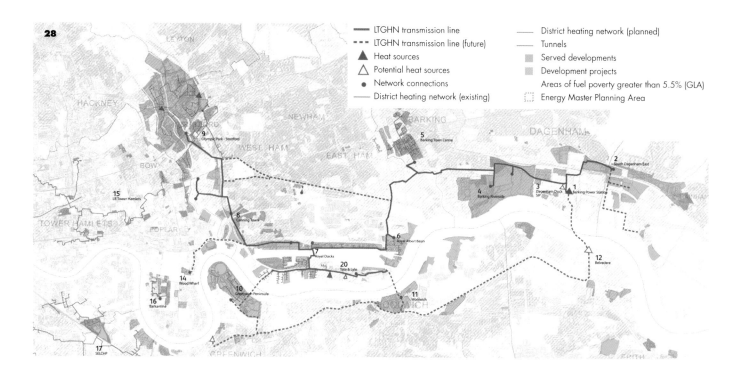

28

- ━━━ LTGHN transmission line
- - - - LTGHN transmission line (future)
- ▲ Heat sources
- △ Potential heat sources
- ● Network connections
- —— District heating network (existing)
- —— District heating network (planned)
- —— Tunnels
- ▪ Served developments
- ▪ Development projects
- Areas of fuel poverty greater than 5.5% (GLA)
- Energy Master Planning Area

had been recently released and clients and design teams were just getting to grips with how to meet it, frequently resorting to biomass solutions. In line with best practice, the ODA required that the 15 per cent be met with passive design measures such as maximising solar gains and daylight where appropriate, increased insulation of the exterior envelope and airtight construction. Good passive design was to be supported by efficient mechanical and electrical systems, with flexible lighting controls and targeted heating, cooling and ventilation. At the time this was challenging current practice. Now with the hindsight of Part L 2010, which required a 25 per cent improvement over 2006, the ODA target is still stretching. It is worth noting, however, that while Part L 2010 permitted CCHP gains to count towards the 25%, the ODA 15% target did not.

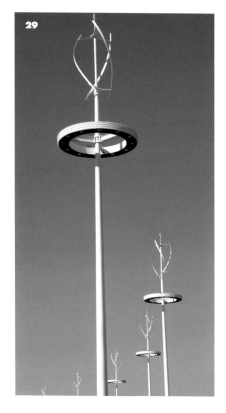

29

Each venue design team was required to submit an energy report at RIBA stages C, D, E and L for review by CLM and Buro Happold. ODA and CLM sustainability team members held regular meetings and workshops with venue design teams to identify energy efficiency measures and ensure that sustainability was not compromised – as it often is – during value engineering. Going a step further, the ODA tried to address the fact that buildings frequently fail to achieve their design targets when operational energy is measured in legacy. Predicted performance targets were written into contracts and regular site inspections were carried out to verify that elements which impact energy efficiency, such as insulation, heating, ventilation and air conditioning (HVAC) equipment and fans, had been procured and installed as specified and to ensure the quality of workmanship and airtightness. It is this attention to detail that is critical to closing the gap between design and performance that occurs on so many buildings, including those with high sustainability aspirations.

The ODA tendered the district heating contract in 2007 and the contract was awarded to Cofely, a subsidiary of GDF-Suez Energy Services, for a 40-year concession to supply the Olympic Park. A district heating system, which represents an approximately £100 million pound investment, supplies the Olympic Park venues, the Olympic and Paralympic Village and the Westfield site via two interconnected energy centres located at the east and west edges of the Park. The Kings Yard Energy Centre houses a 3.3MWₑ CCHP engine, and a nearby Edwardian building, the only existing building retained on the Olympic Park site, houses a 3MWth biomass boiler. The Stratford Energy Centre, which serves the Westfield shopping centre, accommodates two 3.3MWₑ engines. Two 20MWth dual fuel boilers supplement the CCHP to meet peak residential demand morning and evening.

The CCHP engines are currently fuelled by natural gas, which is converted into electricity and hot and chilled water. Water is piped underground via a 40km network to provide heating and hot water to all the permanent venues, as well as cooling to the Handball Arena and the Main Press Centre. Both energy centres include several vacant bays that can accommodate additional plant and alternate technologies as demand increases or lower carbon fuel sources are adopted. In keeping with this strategy of sizing for legacy demand, the LDA and the London Thames Gateway Development Corporation invested £480,000 in April 2011 for Cofely to extend the Olympic Park hot water pipe network to Stratford High Street so that future development can tap into the district heating system.

The downside of the Olympic Park district heating contract is that for 40 years Cofely has the sole right to supply heating to the Park. This rules out the use of any solar thermal or ground source heat technologies on the Park because they reduce heating demand and conflict with the business case for site-wide CCHP. Cofely, subject to strict OfGem requirements,

30 Kings Yard Energy Centre, on the western boundary of the Park near Hackney Wick, occupies an Edwardian building, the only structure retained on the Olympic Park site. It houses a 3MWth biomass boiler, and a visitors' centre that explains the district heating system that is proposed for after the Games.

31 Linear rooflights in the Velodrome provide natural daylight for typical daily use anticipated in legacy.

32 Sunpipes bring daylight into the Handball Arena, reducing lighting requirements.

was only prepared to offer a fossil fuels solution – natural gas – to power the CCHP, because the reliability of a lower carbon solution such as biogas was not yet proven. Adoption of lower carbon or fossil-free technologies in future is possible, but Cofely has no incentive or obligation to switch to a lower carbon solution unless the price of fuel drives the change.

The full range of renewable technologies – large-scale and small-scale wind, biomass, biomass CCHP, hydro power, tidal energy, ground energy, solar PV and solar thermal – were examined for the Olympic Park site using a £/kg CO_2 reduction metric. Infrastructure scale renewables offered the best value for money, and CCHP biomass and large-scale wind were identified as the most suitable approaches. These were viewed as preferable both financially and in terms of carbon reduction.

THE WIND TURBINE

A proposal for a permanent 120m-high wind turbine on the Olympic Park was granted planning permission in September 2007. Members of the design team had travelled to Norway where they had seen large-scale wind turbines in urban settings well established, and the hope was to use the London 2012 project to jumpstart this technology in the UK. The Eton Manor site at the north end of the Park was selected because it was sufficiently far from any housing, a turbine would not cast a shadow on any sporting venues, and its noise would be mitigated by the adjacent A12. However, complications arose as detailed design on the wind turbine progressed.

Safety concerns mounted with UK incidents of a turbine blade falling off and ice throw from a wind turbine. The ODA undertook a risk analysis, which concluded that the statistical probability of someone being killed by a falling blade or ice below the turbine could be reduced to 1 in 1 million by establishing a 42m exclusion zone around the turbine and this was incorporated into the design. In addition, changes to the EU Machinery Directive, which regulates lifts in wind turbines, deemed the proposed lift design non-compliant, and the supplier – unable to resolve this issue in time to meet the programme – withdrew from the project. Because none of the previously shortlisted suppliers were willing to come forward in this climate, plans for a wind turbine were finally cancelled in June 2010.

Though criticised by some as green bling, a large-scale wind turbine would have served as a potent visual symbol for London 2012's ambitious sustainability agenda. The turbine would have been visible throughout the Park, from nearby communities and to passing traffic on the A12. It is unfortunate that a changing regulatory environment and the realities of the marketplace ruled out its viability late in the construction programme.

With the cancellation of the turbine, other renewable technologies were re-examined to see how the ODA's 20 per cent commitment could be met. PV arrays have been installed on the Main Press Centre and the roof of the adjacent car park. With these additional PV installations, approximately 9 per cent of the Park's legacy energy demand is predicted to be supplied by renewable energy.

To make up the shortfall from the initial 20 per cent target, the ODA has invested £1.7m in carbon reduction schemes in the four Host Boroughs adjacent to the Park, which the GLA will deliver on the ODA's behalf. Modelled on London's RE:NEW and RE:FIT schemes, energy efficiency measures such as low-energy lighting, insulation, heating and lighting controls and stand-by switches will be installed in up to 12 local schools and approximately 2,800 homes near the Olympic Park. Though less high-profile than a wind turbine, the silver lining of this energy efficiency refurbishment scheme is immediate tangible investment in the existing communities adjacent to the Park.

————— District heating network
————— District cooling network
--------- Potential extension to district heating network
▭ Energy Centre
◻ Head House
– – – Underground power lines

33 A flexible modular design for the Olympic Energy Centre that could easily accommodate changing technologies was central to the brief.

34 Olympic Park energy distribution network, showing CCHP Energy Centre with district heating and cooling network that serves the Park and adjacent development east of the site.

A SUSTAINABLE URBAN QUARTER FOR EAST LONDON

It is rare in a historic city such as London to have a clear ring-fenced site of the size of the Olympic Park. The momentum of the London 2012 investment provided the catalyst to create a framework for a new urban quarter in the Lea Valley which uses its waterways and landscape feature as a starting point and retains many of its original plot boundaries. It has retained much of the original form, layouts, plot boundaries, waterways and landscape features. The strong environmental agenda that shaped the Olympic Park's landscape and infrastructure sets a new precedent for sustainable masterplanning in the UK.

The basis of the masterplan was to create a new piece of city that would knit previously disconnected neighbourhoods together as it is built out over time. It is much more than a series of sports venues in a park. All the London 2012 buildings, from the sports venues to the Olympic and Paralympic Village, from the infrastructure buildings to the press complex, were located in relation to transport links and how they will fit into the fabric of the future city. They were sited with a view to their long-term role as hubs of activity and community landmarks within this evolving piece of city. If long-term uses could not be justified, temporary venues were erected. The next chapter looks in detail at how London 2012's sustainability agenda shaped individual buildings – both permanent and temporary.

35 Visualisation of 130m-high wind turbine proposed for Eton Manor site to meet the Olympic Park's renewable energy requirement. The wind turbine was abandoned in 2010 when new EU legislation regulating turbines made it impossible to deliver in time for the Games.

Chapter 3

Architecture

The Olympic and Paralympic Games are often about iconic sports venues, but London had broader ambitions. The strategists behind London's bid had pinned their hopes on regeneration and environmental responsibility, yet they knew that compelling visualisations of the proposed Olympic Park would help carry the day. Concurrent with the bid preparation, a design competition was held for the Aquatics Centre, the Park's architectural centerpiece, and Zaha Hadid's highly sculptural scheme was named the winner.

But the Aquatics Centre is the exception on the Olympic Park in being selected primarily for its dramatic forms. The central role of design was acknowledged, and the ODA appointed the LSE's (and ex-GLA) Ricky Burdett as design advisor to the ODA during the procurement process. The aim was to attract the UK's top designers to the London 2012 design competitions. For all the other buildings, sustainability was a central consideration, and as project teams were appointed, the ODA's Sustainable Development Strategy was woven into the detailed design brief for each venue.

Sporting Venues

Sporting venues built specifically for the London 2012 Games include both new and temporary buildings in the Olympic Park and the Lee Valley White Water Centre. The key athletic venues are 'the big three': the Olympic Stadium, the Aquatics Centre and the Velodrome. Both the Olympic Stadium and the Aquatics Centre will reduce in size after the Games. The Handball Arena and Eton Manor will be converted for community use and elite sports in legacy. The Basketball Arena and Water Polo Arenas illustrate how London 2012 pushed the supply chain in the delivery of temporary structures. The strategy was to use as many historic and existing venues as possible, and these are described in the overlay chapter (pp. 218–233).

1. (Previous page) One of London 2012's key moves was to size venues appropriately for long-term use. The Aquatics Centre has two temporary wings (yellow seating at left) of 15,000 additional seats. The building will be reduced to a capacity of 2,500 after the Games.

2. Aerial view of Olympic Stadium looking south towards Canary Wharf.

Olympic Stadium

The Olympic Stadium for the London 2012 Olympic Games and Paralympic Games represents a sea change in Olympic Stadium design. Conceived as largely temporary from the outset, it is a literal reinterpretation of the edict 'less is more'.

An early agreement between the International Olympic Committee and London 2012 determined that the Olympic Stadium would provide a 25,000-capacity venue for British athletics after the Games. As a result, the ODA developed a design brief for a Stadium with 'capacity conversion', which would shrink from a capacity of 80,000 during the Games to a 25,000-capacity venue for athletics in future. This meant that an efficient Stadium design could be tailored to the requirements of a single sport. In short, change the building rather than change the sport. Although football was discussed as the most likely legacy sport from the outset, no team was prepared to commit to take on the Stadium after the Games at the time that the ODA needed to proceed with construction to meet the programme. Therefore, the Stadium proceeded on the premise of a lightweight temporary structure that could be reduced in size after the Games, the optimal decision at the time.

Previous Games had multi-purpose stadia designed to accommodate another sport or multiple sports in legacy. For example, Sydney's stadium was conceived from the outset to host football, rugby and concerts, though it did pioneer London's approach of reducing seat capacity post-Games. Its 115,000 capacity was decreased to 80,000 by removing its two end wings. However, in Australia the most cost-effective construction material proved to be in situ concrete, which meant that the wings had to be removed by jackhammer, stretching the notion of 'temporary'.

DESIGN DEVELOPMENT

By contrast, the entire rationale behind London's Stadium design stemmed from the dual premise of temporary architecture and lightweight construction. Research by architect Populous's sustainable stadia team examined the energy profile of a stadium and found that the ratio of operational to embodied energy in stadia differs significantly from other building types because of their intermittent use. Embodied energy represents upwards of 60 per cent of a stadium's lifetime energy load, which is much greater than for most other building types. Reducing energy therefore meant driving embodied energy down by building a smaller, lighter stadium with low embodied energy materials.

'It took us a while to embrace the temporary,' says Rod Sheard, Senior Principal at Populous. Two early design breakthroughs were critical. First, food and hospitality concessions were pulled out of the Stadium structure and located in temporary pods on the site concourse. This

ENVIRONMENTAL PROFILE

BREEAM (west stand – lower ground level only): Excellent. Remainder of building is temporary and therefore BREEAM not applicable.

Predicted CO_2 emissions reduction beyond Building Regulations Part L 2006: 15.1%

Predicted reduction in potable water consumption: 52%

Recycled content (proportion of secondary materials as percentage of value): 31%

Recycled aggregate (proportion of secondary materials as percentage of mass): 36%

Sustainable transport (delivery of materials by rail/water): 49%

U-values (west stand – lower ground level only)

external walls: 0.3 W/m²K

roof slab: 0.21 W/m²K

floor slab: 0.25 W/m²K

glazing: 2.2 W/m²K

MATERIALS

Main materials: concrete, structural steel, reinforcing steel

Materials with recycled content: in situ and precast concrete, copper slag flooring, concourse decking

Reclaimed materials: steel tubes in roof truss, granite blocks in forecourt landscape

Innovative materials, products and technologies: flooring of copper slag, concourse decking made from 95% recycled materials, PVC with phthalate-free plasticiser (wrap)

3. Exploded axonometric of London 2012 Olympic Stadium design, showing from top: lightweight compression truss roof structure with lighting masts, seating terraces, structure for seating terraces, concrete bowl and ground level with concession pods for food and drink.

reduced fire and ventilation requirements, which meant that both building and concourse size could be smaller. The final Stadium design provides serviced VIP accommodation on the west concourse only. Secondly, the structure for the roof and upper tiers of temporary seating were decoupled from the permanent concrete bowl. Separation of the temporary and permanent structure meant that each could be designed as efficiently as possible. The cumulative impact of this approach is that the London 2012 Olympic Stadium's built volume is significantly smaller than comparable modern stadia. Compliant with the ODA's Inclusive Design Standards, it is also one of the most accessible, with an unprecedented number of wheelchair viewing positions. (1 per cent of viewing positions for the Olympic Games and 2 per cent for the Paralympic Games are wheelchair accessible).

Prior to commencing construction, liaison with the contractor ensured that grading of the site minimised cut and fill and transport of earthworks off site. The concrete bowl for permanent seating was partially buried into the slope of the site and made as compact as possible. Only one concourse serves all 80,000 seats capacity, rare for a stadium of such a large size. A Lego-like 'design for disassembly' approach permeates the design of the superstructure. Steel plates were incorporated into the detail design to visually express the connections and for ease of dismantling. The steel and precast structure for the seating terraces was designed to be dismantled so that all steel connections are bolted rather than welded. Removable

4. Exterior view of Olympic Stadium. The roof structure's compression truss was recalculated to incorporate surplus stock steel tubes which had different dimensions from the original design. This substitution saved time in the programme and reduced the amount of new steel fabricated for the Stadium.

4

glass reinforced concrete caps, nicknamed hedgehogs, enclose the joints at ground level. Aluminium rails are bolted into the 7m-long precast planks that support the seating, and individual seats clip onto the rails. All can be easily removed and reinstated elsewhere. Populous architect Philip Johnson imagines the white seats relocated to various cricket grounds around the country. Buro Happold estimates that approximately two-thirds of the embodied energy of the Stadium can be recovered by reuse.

The designers also sought a lightweight solution for the roof. Computational fluid dynamic modelling and wind tunnel testing were used to determine the extent of roof coverage required to control maximum allowable wind speeds on the track. In the final design, approximately two-thirds of spectators are under cover. Because of the Stadium's elliptical shape and the extent of roof cover required, a lightweight compression truss was possible in lieu of the cantilevered roof structure frequently used for stadia. A cable roof construction with a fabric enclosure was developed, which relies on a compression ring at the Stadium perimeter held in place by radial cables tied to an inner ring, similar to a bicycle wheel. Populous proposed an external fabric wrap to enclose the Stadium and protect spectators from wind and rain. The wrap was based on the notion of a temporary stadium and the fabric specified has, approximately, a five-year lifespan.

5. Study comparing operational and embodied carbon emissions of a typical stadium with other building types.

6. Study comparing embodied energy for different typical stadia designs.

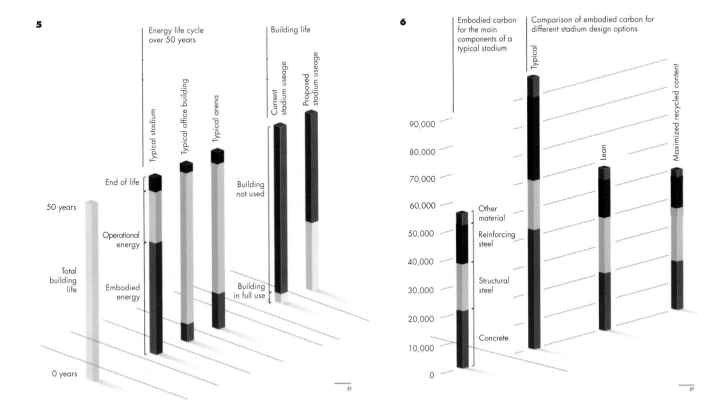

FROM DESIGN TO PROCUREMENT

Although the Stadium's compactness plays the greatest role in reducing its environmental impact, opportunities for reducing embodied energy in materials were examined throughout design and procurement. The Stadium components with the highest embodied energy are steel and concrete. When the time came for the steel subcontractor to order the large tubes for the roof's compression truss, structural steel fabricator Watson Steel succeeded in sourcing redundant stock. This expedited the programme, reduced costs and proved an environmental win.

A stock of surplus steel tubes, larger in diameter and shorter than those specified, was identified. Populous judged the visual change acceptable, and the structural design was modified accordingly. The reclaimed steel had to be tested to establish its grade, and the shorter tube lengths had to be welded together to meet the required 15m spans. Approximately 2,500 tonnes of the steel roof structure's total 3,850 tonnes is made up of redundant stock. The costs of redesign and steel testing were offset by the lower price of the surplus steel and time savings. According to subcontractor Watson Steel, sourcing of surplus steel is not a new practice; what is new is assessing its environmental impact by calculating the savings in embodied energy.

While the use of the surplus steel tubes was largely driven by time savings, the scheduling implications of using reclaimed materials often posed a considerable challenge. Granite blocks reclaimed from King George V Dock during London City Airport expansion works were identified for use in the Stadium's landscape works in 2007, and had to be stored off site by the contractor until they were installed in 2010. The salvaged granite blocks were used both in the riverbank near the Stadium and in the vehicular forecourt in lieu of a 60m-long reinforced concrete retaining wall.

7 The Meccano-like steel structure of the Olympic Stadium has bolted connections to facilitate dismantling.

8 Section of Olympic Stadium west stand.

8

West stand section
1. Compression roof truss made of surplus steel
2. Sports lighting rig
3. Roof membrane
4. Drop-off area
5. Field of play

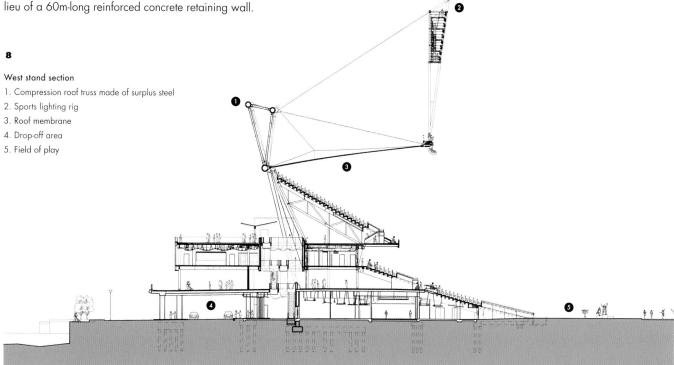

9

Two further examples illustrate how the London 2012 Stadium design drove innovation. Firstly, the main contractor Sir Robert McAlpine (SRM) worked with subcontractor Tarmac to maximise the recycled content of the Stadium's precast seating terraces. The 7.5m-long planks incorporate 30 per cent recycled aggregate made from crushed concrete. Secondly, the use of PVC-based materials for both the roof fabric and the Stadium wrap was a significant departure from conventional environmental practice. PVC has been avoided because of toxic phthalates used in the plasticiser to increase its flexibility. At the Millenium Dome PVC was changed to PTFE due to pressure from Greenpeace. Research by the ODA sustainability team concluded that one of the major issues within the PVC industry was the lack of recycling and, through early engagement with suppliers, demand from London 2012 has driven innovation in the plastics industry. The ODA negotiated a buyback scheme for all temporary PVC used in the Park. Meanwhile, a phthalate-free plasticiser has been developed and though not available in time for the roof fabric because fire testing had not been completed, it has been specified for the wrap and waterproofing and was used on the Water Polo Arena and Basketball Arena.

9 Sketch of timber gridshell concession pods for food and drink proposed for the London 2012 Olympic Stadium site.

London's Olympic Stadium – a lightweight temporary structure designed so that two-thirds of its capacity could be dismantled post-Games – was not future-proofed for conversion to a permanent multi-sport stadium for football or rugby. An ongoing track and field use was agreed with the IOC at the time of the bid. In November 2011, London won the bid to host the International Association of Athletics Federations World Athletics Championship in 2017, based on a seating capacity of 60,000. This ensures an ongoing role for athletics events at the Olympic Stadium over the next five years and potentially longer.

The OPLC will retain ownership of the stadium and is responsible for the legacy transformation. The OPLC plans to identify a legacy operator to lease the stadium by testing the market. Potential uses include sporting and community events and concerts which will complement athletic events.

Seating capacity can be reduced to 60,000 without impacting the concrete tiers or structural steel. The temporary nature of the design means that materials such as the roof fabric, which have been specified for an approximately five-year lifespan, will in due course need to be replaced by more robust materials, if the stadium is retained for the longer term. The upper tier of the west stand would also need to be upgraded for Part L compliance. This particular issue highlights the challenge of future-proofing because additional expenditure is required upfront to enable greater flexibility later, and often a client is not willing to invest more for a hypothetical future. Hospitality provision may also need to be increased.

A major issue to be resolved is the location of the ticket turnstiles and concessions for food and drink. During the Games, the 'island' on which the Stadium is located operates as a venue with ticketing at the bridges while in the long term it would be desirable for the Stadium to remain accessible as part of the Park.

Finally, if the decision is taken to convert the stadium to a permanent building, this would alter whole-life costs and introduces the possibility of environmental technologies such as solar roof fabric or rainwater harvesting, unaffordable in a temporary venue. The Stadium will inevitably retain a high profile within the Queen Elizabeth Olympic Park, as the Olympic Park will be known in legacy. Alterations in keeping with the lightness of the original design would be most consistent with and best promote the strong environmental message of the Games.

KEY POINTS
Build less
Build temporary
Design for dismantling
Specify to reduce embodied energy

10 The extent of the Olympic Stadium roof was calculated to reduce wind speed on the track while using a minimum of materials.

Aquatics Centre

The Aquatics Centre is a structure of eye-catching sculptural form. It is the only London 2012 venue whose architect was selected prior to London winning the bid in 2005, which was previous to the environmental agenda of the Games being fully formulated. The compelling visualisations of its wave-like roof – inspired, according to the architects, by the pools it encloses and its parkland setting – were instrumental in securing the Games for London. With its form a given, structural and services engineers were tasked to deliver as efficient a building as possible.

THE COMPETITION

The Aquatics Centre is the architectural centrepiece of the Olympic Park. Situated in the south-east corner of the Park, it will provide an iconic gateway to the Games and welcome almost 70 per cent of visitors arriving via Stratford station (via Westfield), and Stratford International Station. Despite the emphasis on an environmentally responsive Games, the organisers behind the bid felt the need for a strong architectural form to capture the attention of the IOC, so the LDA held an international design competition for the Aquatics Centre concurrent with the preparation of the bid documents in 2004. Due to a lack of 50m swimming pools in London, the LDA committed to build the Aquatics Centre even if London did not secure the bid. This was also a way to show east Londoners that they stood to gain from the Games coming to London, no matter what.

The brief called for three pools – competition and training pools for swimming, and a diving pool – in a permanent venue with large temporary stands providing additional capacity for the Games. From more than 40 submissions, a jury chaired by Richard Rogers named a shortlist of six, including two practices well known for sustainable design: Bennetts Associates and Behnisch Architekten of Stuttgart. As part of the judging process, the schemes underwent a technical assessment with a particular focus on sustainability and access. The Bennetts Associates scheme, an eighth of the size of the Beijing Water Cube, was notable for its compactness in legacy. Its asymmetrical plan located all the temporary capacity towards the river so that it could be replaced by a landscaped area linking the pools to the river after the Games.

ENVIRONMENTAL PROFILE

BREEAM: Excellent

Predicted CO$_2$ emissions reduction beyond Building Regulations Part L 2006: 15.3% (forecast)

Predicted reduction in potable water consumption: 32%

Recycled content (proportion of secondary materials as percentage of value): 29%

Recycled aggregate (proportion of secondary materials as percentage of mass): 51%

Sustainable transport (delivery of materials by rail/water): 56%

U-values (from Stage F)

wall: 0.25 W/m^{2}K

roof: 0.2 W/m^{2}K

exposed floor: 0.25 W/m^{2}K

glazed facade (overall system): 1.40 W/m^{2}K

MATERIALS

Main materials: concrete, steel, timber

Materials with recycled content: concrete

Recyclable materials: phthalate-free PVC wrap for temporary stands

Innovative materials, products and technologies

High levels of recycled aggregate and ground granulated blast-furnace slag (GGBS) in fair-faced concrete

Targeted services strategy, including low-velocity air through concrete ducts and glazed façade with 'hot water' mullions

Backflushing water for pool used for toilets

Phthalate-free PVC for wrap of temporary stands

11 View from Aquatics Centre main swimming pool up into temporary stand.

Iconic architecture that would catch the eye of the International Olympic Committee carried the day. In late 2004, Zaha Hadid Architects (ZHA) was announced the winner. The competition scheme – approximately twice the size of the final project – included a 300m-long roof that spanned over competition and diving pools, a training pool, a water polo pool and temporary seating stands. The visualisations showed the temporary stands feathered into the building's organic form.

The idea of a One Planet Olympic Games was central to London's bid (see pp. 28–31), yet the specifics of how this impacted on individual venues was yet to be spelled out. Although sustainable design was part of the LDA competition brief, it played no role in the selection of the winning scheme nor was it a driver for the ZHA scheme. After the ODA was established and One Planet principles were translated into design targets, the project underwent a major redesign. A number of changes were implemented to improve the efficiency of the building and reduce the size of the venue. For example, the training pool was relocated under the main bridge approach from Stratford, though it is still within the building. The temporary wings were pulled out from under the main roof and reconceived as orthogonal plug-ins that could be hired off-the-shelf and sold on or reused after the Games. These changes reduced the size of the proposed building by approximately half, but the building's symmetrical design and double curvature long span roof were retained.

DESIGN DEVELOPMENT

The ODA's sustainability targets combined with the target for BREEAM Excellent rating meant that the project team had to overlay an environmental strategy on the existing design. The design team's focus – and rightly so – was to make the legacy building as efficient as possible. Alternative structural approaches, including an arch, a timber structure and the introduction of columns to shorten the spans, were explored to reduce the amount of embodied carbon in the roof. Timber proved inappropriate for the long spans, and the arch was rejected because it increased the building's interior volume and adversely impacted the programme. The use of intermediate columns was ruled out because they restricted views of the pool. The final height and roof curvature of the permanent pool hall were determined by the sight lines from the last row of the temporary stand to the pool and diving platforms, creating a vast pool hall driven by Games' requirements. Ironically, the temporary stands, the very feature of the project that make its ultimate size more appropriate in legacy, also determine the height of the roof.

12 Longitudinal section of the Aquatics Centre. The double curvature roof and the volume of the pool hall are visually spectacular, but increase the embodied carbon and the volume of space to be conditioned.

1. Plaza bridge
2. Olympic Family lounge
3. Training pool
4. Diving pool
5. Chiller plant rooms
6. Main entrance stair
7. Roof structure

12

Longitudinal section (Olympic mode)

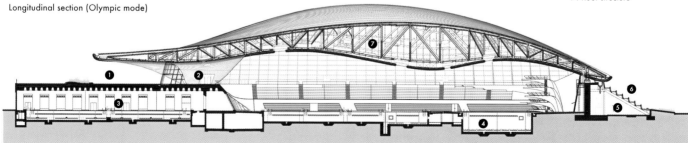

THE ROOF'S STRUCTURAL DESIGN

The swooping form of the Aquatics Centre's roof is the building's most memorable feature. Supported on only three points – a wall in the south and two concrete cores at the north end of the building – the dramatic double curvature roof over the pool hall is 160m long and up to 80m wide at its widest point. Its genesis is sculptural form, and the solution is driven by buildability and budget, not structural efficiency.

Steel fan trusses, whose bottom members form a double curve over the diving and competition pools, run north–south between the concrete supports. The outer trusses on each side of the building cantilever upwards to span the openings for the temporary stands. In addition, a 3m by 3m grid of structural steel purlins spans above and below the fan trusses to achieve the required curvatures for the roof decking and timber ceiling. Due to both the double curvature and the three-point support, the steel tonnage in the trusses is about 25 per cent more than a rule of thumb would indicate for an efficient span of this length, according to Arup, and this is not counting the purlins.

TEMPORARY STANDS

Use of temporary stands is a key strategy for creating a swimming venue that can accommodate the Games and be appropriately scaled for community use in the future. It is worth noting that the level of ambition in terms of incorporating temporary stands into a permanent building on a constrained site differentiates London's Aquatics Centre from those of prior Games. Beijing's Water Cube, transformed by a Canadian developer into a water park, retains its full volume; Sydney's pool featured an open-air temporary stand and Athens had an open-air pool.

To make the building leaner, the curved temporary stands of the competition were simplified in the hopes of utilising off-the-shelf stands that could be reused. However, the Aquatics

13 One of the six schemes shortlisted for the Aquatics Centre competition, submitted by Bennetts Associates. This unsuccessful scheme located the building to the eastern site boundary to maximise outdoor space on the river in legacy. A single tier of temporary seating was proposed to increase the capacity during the Games.

14 View from main pool hall into welcome zone. The visual concrete for fair-faced areas used three different mixes, depending on structural performance requirements and desired visual effect.

Centre's constrained site between the Waterworks River on the west and Carpenters Road on the east meant that the temporary stands had to overhang the road. This necessitated a bespoke steel solution at the lower level. The use of a hire element for the upper stands was explored but rejected because the complexity of marrying off-the-shelf components with a bespoke structure below proved too costly. The temporary stand is entirely bespoke, with no specific plan for the reuse of the steel structure or the seating, though they can be easily dismantled and reused. The stands are enclosed by a phthalate-free PVC wrap that will be reclaimed by the manufacturer.

A further complication arose from the performance requirements of the temporary stands. Because they must be complete a year ahead of the Games to accommodate test events, some of which are scheduled in winter, panels of insulation had to be added to maintain poolside temperatures. While the aspiration of using temporary stands is a good idea in principle, the reality proved much more complex. Despite the complications, the use of temporary stands does mean a more appropriately sized legacy building, which requires a smaller plant and consumes less operational energy in use after the Games.

DAYLIGHTING AND SOLAR GAIN

The constraints of the site and the pool dimensions dictated a linear solution with a long south-western exposure. The UK climate means that heating is required for most of the year to maintain the pool at its required temperature, and solar gain can partially meet this demand. Optimal glazing orientation and size for solar gain were not a driver in the architectural solution. Had solar orientation been a major driver from the outset, solar gain could have been optimized by providing the appropriate amount of glazing on each elevation. The design team had to make the best of the symmetrical glazing layout. Fritting, which is necessary to control glare on the pool and diving platforms, further reduces solar gain.

Simultaneously with the design of individual venues, a Park-wide strategy for district heating was developed. Because the Aquatics Centre requires almost year-round heating to maintain the required temperature in the pools, it plays an important role in the district heating system by providing a heat sink. The pools provide an outlet for the district heating system to reject heat even in summer.

SERVICING STRATEGY

The servicing strategy for the pool hall is governed primarily by the requirement to maintain the pool water at 29°C, which means that the air at poolside must also be heated. In contrast with a conventional HVAC approach for a large sports venue, which would typically employ high-level ducts with fans to condition the entire volume, the Aquatics Centre is treated as three different microclimates – poolside, seating tiers and glazed façade. This approach complements the main pool hall's dramatic architectural volume because it is entirely

15 The roof structure is supported on just three points: a wall at the south end (1) and two concrete cores to the north (2). The fan trusses (3) run in a north-south direction and are shaped to clear the diving and competition pools. The two outer trusses (4) act as inclined tied arches which create two cantilevered wings on either side of the building for the temporary seating.

16 (Overleaf) Aquatics Centre pool hall in Games mode with temporary stands. The 12,000 square metre ceiling is lined with FSC-certified Brazilian red louro. Supplier FinnForest developed a plywood laminated with red louro that could withstand humidity levels in the pool to reduce the quantities of hardwood required.

15

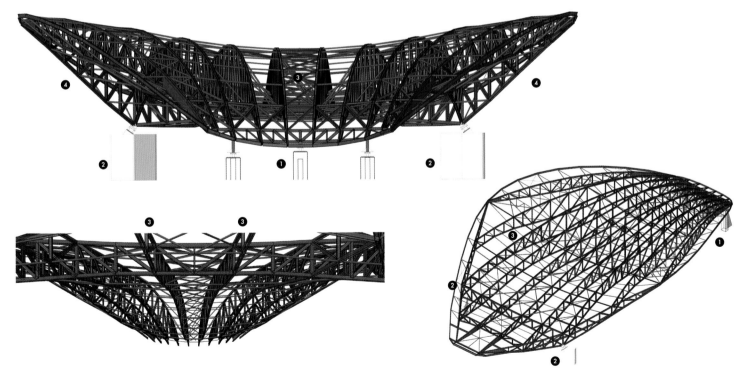

integrated – no ducts are visible anywhere. Because the steel roof structure is continuously wrapped, penetrations, and therefore infiltration, are minimized. The air permeability target for the main pool hall is $5m^3/m^2/hr$ @ 50 Pa.

To keep heating demand and fan use to a minimum, services are targeted to meet the performance requirements of the different zones. The poolside is conditioned by a low-velocity air system supplied through concrete ducts below the pool deck that feeds into a plenum beneath the seating tiers. Poolside supply air enters through louvres in the vertical wall below the seating tier, and friction loss is kept to a minimum due to a large plenum and low velocity supply. The cool surface of the pool water draws this air down, creating a cycle of air movement just over the pool surface that is then extracted through louvres in the drainage channel, enabling chemicals in the air due to chlorination to be drawn off at low level rather than mixed with the air of the pool hall. A radiant floor (underfloor heating) provides additional heating at poolside. A separate plant with air handling units and ammonia chillers provides supplementary heating and cooling for the seating tiers as necessary. A third zone that requires targeted conditioning is the glazed legacy façade, which must be maintained at 23°C to avoid condensation. An integrated hot water system in the mullions of the glazed façade, supplied by German manufacture Seele, will regulate the air temperature adjacent to the glazing to control condensation on the legacy glazing. The roof, which is insulated with 200mm of continuous insulation, contains additional heaters to prevent downdraughts.

The use of PVs across the entire roof was examined. It would have added approximately £1.5 million to £2 million to the budget while only providing 5 per cent of predicted energy demand. Extra insulation provided greater value for money than renewables.

17 Cross-section of Aquatics Centre in Olympic Games mode with temporary stands. The sight line from the back row of the temporary stand was a major determinant of the height of the pool hall roof.

18 Visualisation of final appearance of the Aquatics Centre in legacy after the temporary seating stands for the Games have been removed.

19 Cross-section of Aquatics Centre in legacy mode. Glazing encloses the openings where the temporary stands slotted into the building. Mullions with an integrated hot water system have been specified to control condensation on the glazing because a targeted services strategy means that the volume of the pool hall is conditioned at poolside only.

17

Cross-section (Olympic mode)

1. Main competition pool
2. General spectator stand
3. Media and spectator stand
4. Concourse area
5. Toilets
6. Divers' warm-up
7. Roof structure

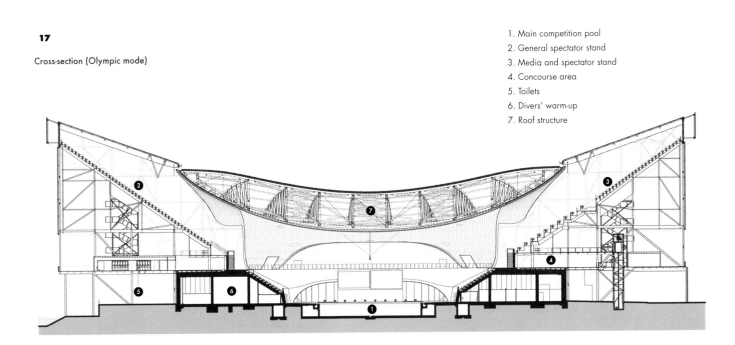

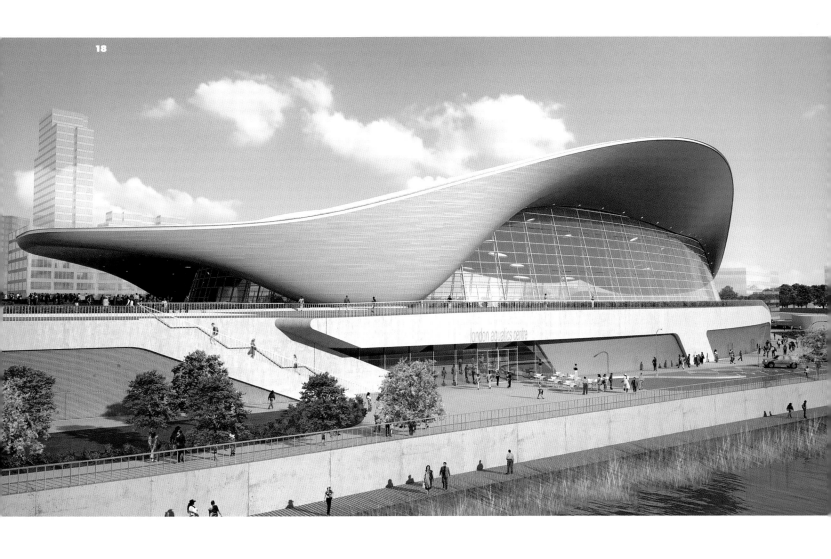

19

Cross-section (legacy mode)

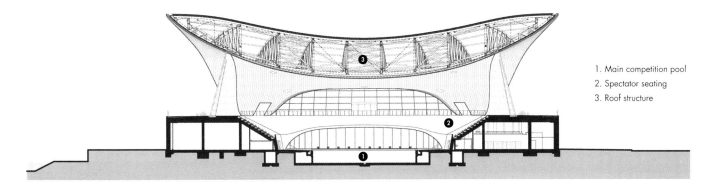

1. Main competition pool
2. Spectator seating
3. Roof structure

WATER

Water use in the Aquatics Centre is primarily determined by shower demand, which could be up to 75 per cent in legacy depending on the building's popularity. As in all the venues for the Games, low-flow fittings are specified as standard. Water in all three pools is continually recirculated and passes through sand filtration tanks to maintain water quality. An innovation at the Aquatics Centre is that when water is drained from the sand filtration tanks so that the filters can be cleaned, the water is recovered and used for toilet flushing. This is estimated to reduce water demand for the building by 3 per cent. A small rainwater harvesting system has been provided to irrigate the green roof over the plant room at the southern end of the building.

MATERIALS

Because the Aquatics Centre has a 3,700m^2 basement and three pools, the volume of concrete in the building far exceeds that of the other venues. In addition, below grade transfer bridging structures that span two high voltage infrastructure tunnels under the building resulted in the largest single concrete pour on the Olympic Park. Seven different structural concrete mixes were used. According to ZHA associate director Jim Heverin, a major lesson for the architects – already being applied on other projects – was the excellent visual quality that can be achieved in fair-faced concrete using up to 100 per cent recycled aggregate and up to 50 per cent cement substitution.

'The embodied carbon in the concrete was a key consideration. The Aquatics Centre can't be compared to the other venues, which are flat tracks without basements; we have three pools surrounded by plant rooms. We had never used this amount of GGBS in fairfaced concrete. One of the big lessons is that you can achieve excellent visual quality.'

JIM HEVERIN, ASSOCIATE DIRECTOR, ZAHA HADID ARCHITECTS

20 Aerial view of Aquatics Centre temporary stands with 15,000 seats under construction.

21 Interior view of Aquatics Centre pool hall with concrete diving platforms. Conditioning is supplied through low-velocity concrete ducts below the pool deck so that the architectural integrity of the Brazilian red louro timber ceiling is uninterrupted.

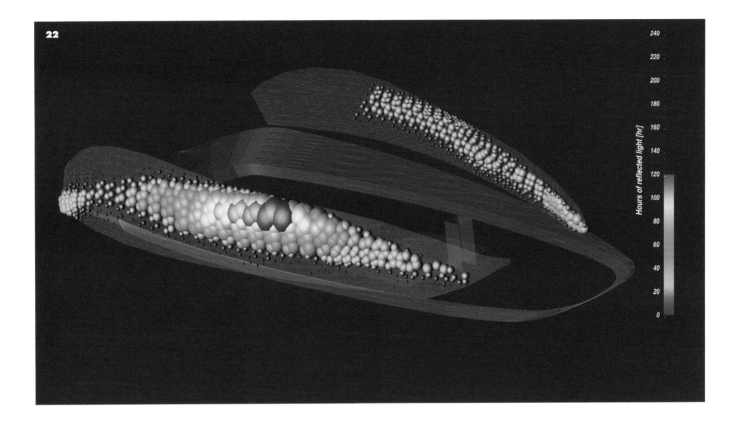

Hours of reflected light [hr]

240
220
200
180
160
140
120
100
80
60
40
20
0

Brazilian red louro supplied by FinnForest lines the ceiling of the pool hall and the interior soffits. Hardwood is used on the exterior soffits. To reduce the quantities of red louro required, FinnForest developed a laminated plywood for the ceiling interior. Every step of the chain of custody from the Brazilian forest to FinnForest's plant in Germany to the Olympic Park site was documented and audited. The timber was also pre-cut and sized to fit in order to avoid offcuts and wastage.

AN OLYMPIC STANDARD SWIMMING VENUE FOR EAST LONDON

The Aquatics Centre will provide a dramatic focus to the southern end of the Queen Elizabeth Olympic Park, which together with the ArcheloMittal Orbit is likely to draw people into the Park from Westfield, Stratford City and beyond. With its sculptural concrete diving platforms, the pool hall will project well on television screens across the globe during the Games and, if well programmed, well managed and reasonably priced, is likely to prove a popular swimming venue in the long run.

The strategy of designing a building with temporary stands so that it could be downsized for legacy is a sound one. However, the challenge of a constrained site meant that delivering temporary stands with components readily available on the hire market proved more complex than anticipated.

22 Daylighting studies were used to determine the fritting on the legacy glazing to eliminate glare on the pool. The contrast between the amount of reflected daylight on the south and north fenestration is clearly evident.

23 Aerial view of Aquatics Centre temporary stands almost complete, showing constrained site with stands cantilevered over river. A small green roof encloses the southern plant room, and the Water Polo Arena is visible to the north.

24 After the Games, seating capacity will be reduced from 17,500 to just 2,500 permanent seats.

To be consistent with the spirit of an environmentally responsible Games, it should have been possible to weight the importance of sustainability at competition stage to result in a signature low carbon swimming centre to showcase sustainable design. An Aquatics Centre by its very nature has a greater embodied carbon footprint than other Olympic sports venues due to the concrete structure required to enclose multiple swimming pools compared with the lightweight fields of play for other sports. Pools also require heating throughout the year. Incorporation of sustainable design principles into the design of the Aquatics Centre was partially a victim of its early timing. Its dramatic tripod structure and its soaring interior volume were conceived as a sculptural set piece and then retrofitted with energy-saving measures. Integrated design from concept stage is a much more effective way to achieve a low carbon building. Its temporary stands and extensive trialling of lower carbon concrete mixes (see pp. 100–105) are nonetheless noteworthy contributions to the lexicon of sustainable design.

KEY POINTS

Role of iconic architecture in place-making in Olympic Park

An appealing venue for legacy

Integrated design from the outset preferable to adapting a building already designed

Temporary 'wings', while a plus for legacy, complex to deliver

Pools provide heat sink for Park-wide district heating

CONCRETE PROCUREMENT: A CASE STUDY

In terms of mass, concrete was the second most widely used material on the Olympic Park after engineered fills. The ODA recognised early on that an assured supply of concrete was critical to meeting London 2012's construction programme. Use of a single Park-wide supplier with an on-site batching plant would minimise the risk of delays due to irregular deliveries and offered significant sustainability wins. Lower embodied energy mixes that incorporate cement substitutions and recycled aggregate could be offered in bulk across the Park to different contractors, and the location of the plant adjacent to a rail head would reduce embodied energy related to transport. In the end, an impressive 94 per cent of materials related to concrete production (by mass) were delivered to the Olympic Park site by rail.

In the procurement process for a concrete supplier, sustainability comprised 20 per cent of the weighting of the technical assessment in the tenders, far exceeding conventional contracts where it is typically a maximum of 5 per cent and frequently non-existent. Tenderers were asked to consider targets for recycled aggregate, cement substitution, sustainable transport of materials to site and use of low-emission vehicles. London Concrete, a subsidiary of Aggregate Industries, was appointed in December 2007, and all contractors on the Olympic Park were required to source concrete from the on-site plant. A member of CLM's Sustainability Team was assigned to manage this process and CLM's technical support and workshops with project teams were critical to the success of this approach.

Approximately 30 main concrete mixes were used on the Olympic Park. The bespoke BREEAM assessments specified minimum requirements for cement substitution: 40 per cent PFA or 70 per cent GGBS in substructure and 30 per cent PFA or 55 per cent GGBS in superstructure. The ODA opted to promote the use of PFA because it is a waste product from the UK's coal-fired plants that often ends up in landfills, while much GGBS had to be imported. However, architects tend to specify GGBS because it yields a lighter colour, so London Concrete offered both options.

CEMENT SUBSTITUTION AND RECYCLED AGGREGATE

The majority of superstructure concrete in the Olympic Park was in self-finishing fair-faced applications. The Aquatics Centre team poured trial mixes to test different quantities of GGBS substitution ranging from 30 per cent to 70 per cent before establishing 40 per cent as the maximum to achieve the desired visual quality.

ODA research showed that transportation was the key factor determining the embodied energy of aggregates. WRAP guidance promotes the use of primary aggregate when the source of recycled aggregate is more than 30km further from the site than virgin aggregate. Due to its ample supply and consistent quality, London Concrete's preferred source of recycled aggregate was stent, a china waste byproduct from Cornwall. Although the source of stent was approximately 250km further away than a source of primary aggregate near the Olympic Park site, it could be supplied by rail.

Initially, lack of familiarity with stent and concerns about strike times and finishes meant that project teams were more willing to adopt it in substructure applications such as pilings and

25 Training pool ceiling with coffers. High-strength concrete was required to suit the 120-year design life durability due to the building's double function as a bridge. The mix had 60 per cent GGBS with 10 per cent china clay stent aggregate, which was shipped to the Olympic Games site by rail from Cornwall.

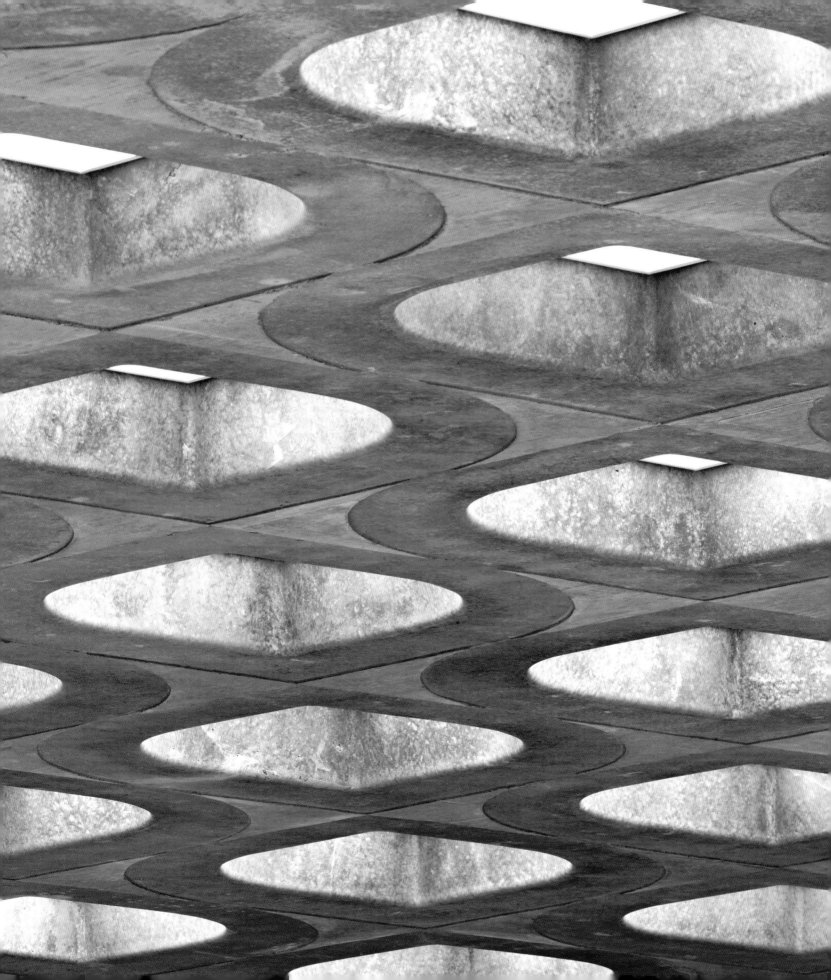

foundations than in visible locations. This reluctance diminished significantly over the lifetime of the Olympic Park's construction as contractors learned from each other. The Olympic Stadium, the first venue to go on site, adopted quality benchmarks recommended by their subcontractor without any site trials of alternative mixes. At the Aquatics Centre, meeting the ODA's target of 25 per cent aggregate substitution was more difficult because the concrete for the swimming pools, which comprise about one third of the concrete in the venue, required a virgin limestone aggregate with a lower coefficient of thermal expansion than stent, to minimise the risk of cracking. To meet the ODA targets, the Aquatics Centre team increased the coarse aggregate substitution in other concrete areas to 76 per cent, setting a new benchmark and addressing concern from other project teams about the visual quality of fair-faced concrete with coarse aggregate substitutions. Ground floor slabs and structural cores on the IBC, the podium topping at the Stadium, the Eton Manor sub-structure, and a brushed concrete pathway on the Greenway were subsequently poured with 100 per cent stent replacement.

PRECAST CONCRETE

The use of an on-site batching plant meant that only about 5 per cent of the concrete used on the Olympic Park was precast. The traditional advantages of precast (reducing the construction programme, quality control and reduced waste) were compensated for by the availability of a well-managed ready mix-supply.

26 Scoreboard wall in the Aquatics Centre (in background). In the wall application, a greater percentage of GGBS and more recycled aggregate were employed. Cement substitution reached 40 per cent GGBS and 76 per cent china clay stent.

27 Detail of dive-boards in the Aquatics Centre. A concrete mix that would limit thermal movement and minimise cracking was essential for the dive-boards. A self-compacting concrete with 30 per cent GGBS was used. In terms of aggregates, 10 per cent carboniferous limestone was used to ease concrete placement and limit thermal expansion.

26

27

Where precast concrete was specified, contractors were asked to challenge their supply chain by requesting the use of cement substitutions and recycled aggregates. The bespoke BREEAM requirements for precast were 15 per cent PFA or 30 per cent GGBS. Where recycled aggregates were supplied, the source tended to be crushed precast components from the supplier's yard. For the Velodrome, the precast manufacturer, located near Cambridge, found the nearest source of recycled aggregate was Cornwall, while virgin aggregate was available adjacent to the plant. When contractor ISG calculated the carbon emissions of the transport, the ODA agreed to waive the requirement.

Knowledge sharing was facilitated by centralised technical support through CLM. Precast seating terraces for the Stadium were successfully specified with 25 per cent recycled aggregate. As a result, the infrastructure team pushed its supply chain and was able to deliver 33 per cent recycled aggregate in the temporary precast bridge decks.

The assumption that precast concrete is inherently more sustainable than ready mix concrete was challenged by the experience at the Olympic Park. Because precast yards are highly dependent on curing times to turn over their moulds to maintain productivity and profitability, there is a tendency to increase cementitious content when cement substitutions and recycled aggregates are used, thereby increasing embodied energy. To achieve an optimal mix, all these issues must be balanced.

According to ODA calculations, Park-wide savings on embodied carbon associated with the Olympic Park's concrete strategy are approximately 24 per cent compared to the industry average. The two key factors determining these savings were cement substitution and the use of sustainable transport.

28 Welcome zone ceiling in the Aquatics Centre. Similar to the training pool ceiling, this area had to meet the requirements for a 120-year design life so a similar mix with 60 percent GGBS and 10 per cent stent was used.

29 Diveboard with FSC-certified Brazilian Louro ceiling beyond. In addition to its environmental advantages over cement, GGBS was used to reduce pour temperature, and carboniferous limestone was used to reduce the coefficient of thermal expansion and reduce cracking.

30 Diveboard used self-compacting concrete with 30% GGBS replacement cement content and 10mm carboniferous limestone aggregate to ease concrete placement.

Velodrome

The Velodrome epitomises sustainable design at its best. An integrated approach to architecture, structure and services from the outset produced a building that is both beautiful and efficient. The external envelope and double curvature roof can be imagined as a 'shrink-wrap' around the cycling track, minimising the building's internal volume – and the cubic metres of air to be conditioned. Carefully considered rooflights and natural ventilation further reduce energy loads.

The Velodrome – along with the Handball Arena – is one of two athletic venues in the Olympic Park designed from the outset to be an entirely permanent building. All of its 6,000 capacity will remain after the Games. The Velodrome, designed by Hopkins Architects, benefited from input at design stage by the Lee Valley Regional Park Authority (LVRPA), which operated a cycle circuit on the site prior to redevelopment and will be the building's owner and end user. This dual brief called for a building that could accommodate the exacting demands of Olympians and Paralympians, but that was not overly complex for LVRPA to operate going forward. The Velodrome's anticipated occupancy pattern in the future contrasts markedly with its peak use during the Games. The LVRPA business plan assumes daily use by small school groups and amateur cyclists, larger groups at the weekends and approximately six annual events that would fill the majority of seats.

A particular environmental challenge is cyclists' requirements for temperatures of 26–28°C on the track, which enables them to shave milliseconds off their times due to lower air density. This means that the servicing strategy has to provide a warm environment at the track, while simultaneously maintaining spectator comfort in the upper tiers. With the exception of the Olympic and Paralympic Games, indoor cycling is primarily a winter sport so the heating strategy is of paramount importance.

Faced with these competing challenges, the design team sought to create an intimate viewing experience around the 250m-long track. Seating was divided into an upper and lower gallery, so that with smaller audiences the building would not feel so empty. The notion of a building that exuded cycling in its leanness led to the concept of a cycling track with a lightweight structure with minimal internal volume and nothing superfluous.

ENVIRONMENTAL PROFILE

BREEAM: Excellent

Predicted CO$_2$ emissions reduction beyond Building Regulations Part L 2006: 32% (forecast)

Predicted reduction in potable water consumption: 75%

Recycled content (proportion of secondary materials as percentage of value): 28.6%

Recycled aggregate (proportion of secondary materials as percentage of mass): 20.2%

Sustainable transport (delivery of materials by rail/water): 78%

U-values

bowl: 0.15 W/m^{2}K

glazing: 1.3 W/m^{2}K

roof: 0.15 W/m^{2}K

floor slab: 0.24 W/m^{2}K

MATERIALS

Main materials: concrete, steel and timber

Materials with recycled content: aggregate in situ and precast concrete, wall insulation with 80% recycled content from windscreens, blocks with 75% recycled content

Reclaimed materials: none

Innovative materials, products and technologies: cable-net roof structure with bespoke timber cassette roof, modular approach to services provision

31 The Velodrome's soaring roof form is a result of integrated design between architect and structural and environmental engineers.

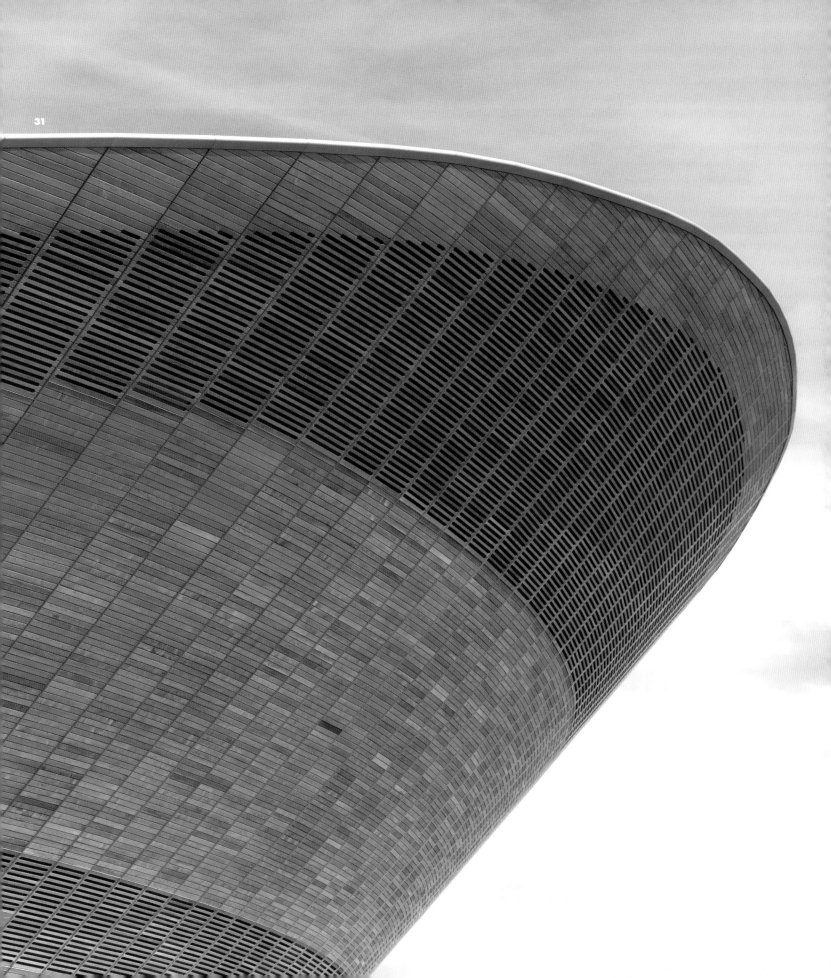

Glazing at Park concourse level, which would enable views into the Velodrome, was another early design concept. The intention was to create a venue that would sit comfortably in the Park setting after the Games and have lasting appeal, attracting casual users such as families and dog walkers, as well as cyclists.

DESIGN DEVELOPMENT

Given the relatively few days of full spectator capacity anticipated for the Velodrome after the Games, the possibility of an unheated venue was initially explored. When thermal modelling by the environmental engineers ruled this out, the design team opted for a highly insulated building. Through an iterative design process between architect, structural engineer and environmental engineer, the Velodome's overall form was honed and refined. From competition stage to final building, over 35,000 cubic metres were removed from its internal volume, reducing it by 15 per cent.

The scheme had to respect the original envelope, which had received planning approval for the bid, but as the design developed the costs and complexities of excavation and ground contamination on the site meant that the building had to be moved by about 40m. This provided Hopkins Architects and the team with the opportunity to reconsider the building's overall massing with two important changes: straight external walls replaced the original curvilinear form, and the relationship with the BMX track was improved. The building also had to be raised by 1.6m due to the ground conditions, yet every attempt was made to reduce the scale of the 22m-high building and integrate it with the surrounding Park. This was part of a strategy to make the most of the synergy between the various types of cycling and concentrate activity on the site to create a cycling hub, which would attract a wide variety of users to the northern part of the Park after the Games.

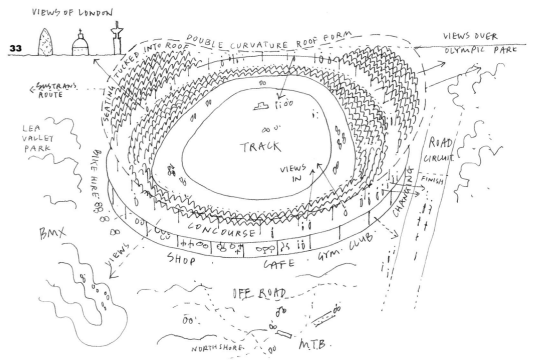

VIEWS OF LONDON

33

DOUBLE CURVATURE ROOF FORM

VIEWS OVER OLYMPIC PARK

SEATING TUCKED INTO ROOF

SUSTRANS ROUTE

LEA VALLEY PARK

BIKE HIRE

BMX

VIEWS

SHOP

TRACK

VIEWS IN

CONCOURSE

CAFE · GYM · CLUB

ROAD CIRCUIT

CHANGING

FINISH

OFF ROAD

NORTHSHORE

M.T.B.

THE ROOF

The most innovative aspect of the Velodrome is its use of a tensile cable-net roof structure, typically used with a lightweight fabric but in this case combined with a fully-insulated roof enclosure. While not directly linked to the building's environmental performance, its lightness and low embodied energy are. The choice of roof was made possible by the engagement of contractor ISG during RIBA Stage C. Initial costing had indicated that a conventional steel structure was most economical, but ISG commissioned a report comparing four roof options: glulam, glulam and cable, all cable and conventional steel. Not only did the all-cable option mean a cost saving of £1.5 million and cut 20 weeks off the programme, but it also used less steel than conventional steel arches and required approximately half the tonnage of concrete in the building's substructure.

The cable-net is held in place by a compression ring that – akin to a tennis racket in the form of a rollercoaster – dips 8m in the middle and rises up 4m at the ends, resulting in an overall depth of 12m. In contrast with the large diameter compression rings typically used in sports structures, the diameter of the Velodrome's compression ring is kept to a minimum because it is rigidly connected to the concrete bowl below. Prefabricated timber cassettes are bolted to plates at each node where the cables cross, and the bespoke node design allows for individual movement of each. Although initially insulation was to be incorporated into the roof cassettes, concerns about condensation and the need to retain clear separation of contracts and liabilities meant that a continuous waterproof membrane, then insulation and a standing seam aluminium roof were built up over the cassettes.

PVs were considered but ruled out primarily due to cost, but also due to increased weight on the long-span, lightweight roof structure.

34

32 The timber-clad bowl of the Velodrome floats over a band of glazing that enables passersby to see into the track.

33 An early concept sketch of the Velodrome showing the double curvature roof, upper and lower seating tiers and concourse glazing.

34 Aerial view of the Velodrome with the rooflights and glazed concourse level clearly visible.

HEATING AND VENTILATION

Nothing in the Velodrome's services design is technically unusual, but the targeted servicing strategy nevertheless makes a vital contribution to the building's superior environmental performance. The approach relies on tailoring heating supply and ventilation to the dual requirement of a warm track environment for cyclists and spectator comfort in the seating tiers. The double curvature architectural form complements the building's environmental performance by creating a natural stack effect for extracting warm air at the two high points through louvres in the cladding.

Underfloor heating supplies the track and maintains a base comfort level in the lower seating tiers. Located under the upper tier of seats, modular air handling units (AHUs) sit just behind the façade in a plenum. In natural ventilation mode, fresh air enters through the louvres in the timber cladding and moves through the plenum to supply vents in the risers of the seating tiers. The mechanical plant is located in this same plenum, under the seating tier rather than in a remote plant room to minimise duct runs. The AHUs also feed jet nozzles in the floor of the upper tier to provide rapid response heating as necessary in winter. In summer, the main Velodrome space is naturally ventilated without the use of any fans, and cooling is supplied only in the offices and server room.

35 An interior view of the daylit track in the Velodrome. Rooflights provide adequate daylighting for most day-to-day training in legacy. More than 360 fittings can provide elevated lighting levels up to 2,000 lux for major events.

36 Exploded diagram of cladding showing the lightweight roof structure and ventilation louvres and plenum.

37 Environmental diagrams illustrating approaches to ventilation, daylighting, rainwater harvesting and insulation.

35

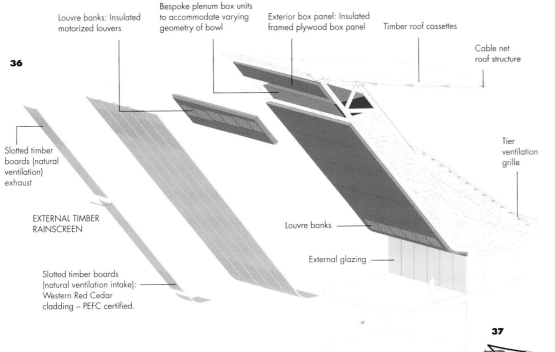

36

Louvre banks: Insulated
motorized louvers

Bespoke plenum box units
to accommodate varying
geometry of bowl

Exterior box panel: Insulated
framed plywood box panel

Timber roof cassettes

Cable net
roof structure

Slotted timber
boards (natural
ventilation)
exhaust

EXTERNAL TIMBER
RAINSCREEN

Tier
ventilation
grille

Louvre banks

External glazing

Slotted timber boards
(natural ventilation intake):
Western Red Cedar
cladding – PEFC certified.

The use of 20 smaller AHUs rather than two large ones means that they can be operated
to meet demand when the building is partially occupied, further reducing energy loads and
operational costs. 3D modelling of the plant installation was essential to fit the mechanical
equipment in the constrained irregular space.

DAYLIGHT

Provision of daylight represents a significant departure from the typical shed design of most
velodromes. The configuration of rooflights was carefully studied to provide a uniform level of
300 lux, adequate for the building to be used without additional lighting during most days.
To avoid glare, laminated glass with milky white polyvinyl butyral (PVB) interlayers that allow
approximately 30 per cent light transmission was specified.

MATERIALS

Early contractor engagement also meant an unusually long lead time – eight months – to
assess material choices and consider how best to meet the ODA's sustainability targets,
including delivery of materials by rail and water. The choice of roof structure, the selection
of concrete mixes and the timber sourcing all benefited from early involvement by both
contractor and subcontractors. The cable-net roof offered multiple advantages: cost savings,
a shortened programme, lower embodied energy and improved health and safety conditions
because of minimal working at height compared to a conventional steel roof. These only
became clear through ISG's involvement of subcontractors.

37

Natural ventilation

Mechanical ventilation + heating

Daylight

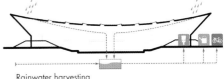

Rainwater harvesting

High insulation

ARCHITECTURE **111**

Concrete

The Velodrome utilised five different in situ concrete mixes, all supplied by the batching plant on the Olympic Park. Each mix had a different percentage of recycled aggregate and cement substitute, depending on the desired performance and appearance. With ISG involvement, the layout of plywood for shuttering was also rationalised to reduce waste from 20 per cent down to just 3 per cent. When undertaken at design stage, consideration of standard materials sizes can lead to considerable cost and material savings.

Timber

Two primary types of timber are used on the Velodrome: western red cedar from Canada for the cladding and Siberian pine for the track. In line with ODA requirements, both are FSC certified. While the FSC certification was straightforward for the Canadian wood, it was extremely time-consuming for the Siberian Pine, which was selected by the track joiner for its tall straight trees. Timber supplier Arnold Laver was responsible for obtaining certificates to prove the chain of custody from Siberia to the Olympic Park via Germany where the timber was milled.

Water

To meet the ODA's target for a 40 per cent reduction in potable water consumption, the Velodrome uses water-efficient fittings and rainwater harvesting. Calculations demonstrated that collection from half of the 13,000 m² roof was adequate to meet demand. The harvested water supplies toilets and landscape irrigation.

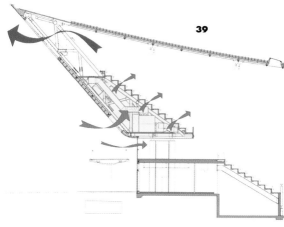

Natural Ventilation mode (summer)

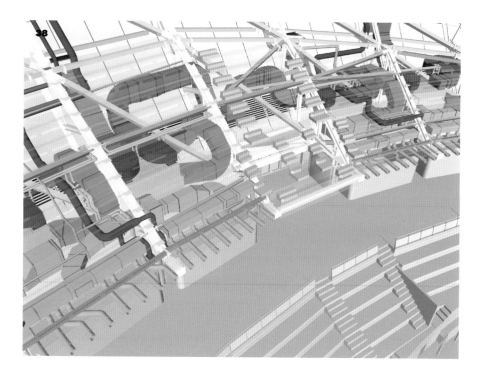

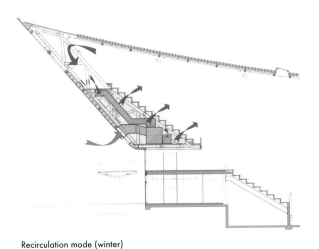

Recirculation mode (winter)

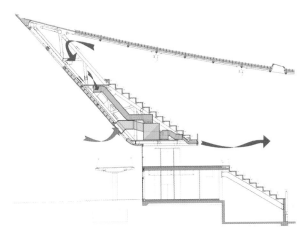

Boost heating mode

Although a whole-life cost assessment showed that the capital costs associated with the system would not be paid back by savings in water charges, the system was nevertheless installed to reduce water demand. Due to contaminated ground conditions, the 25 m³ tank is located in a ground-floor plant room. Two columns at the west end of the track enclose the rainwater pipes that supply the tank.

Transporting materials

Some 78 per cent of all construction materials for the Velodrome were delivered by rail, well exceeding the ODA's 50 per cent target. Delivery by barge proved to be unfeasible because it would have necessitated multiple handling from lorry to barge.

SUSTAINABLE DESIGN IS GOOD DESIGN

The Velodrome sets an important marker for sustainable design because its form, structure and environmental strategy reinforce each other to create exceptional architecture. It is important to note that the Velodrome surpasses the ODA's sustainability targets without the use of any renewables – aside from the Park-wide district heating – proof that a low carbon building does not have to be high-tech to perform well.

38 3D modelling of the mechanical plant and the ducts in the plenum below the seating tiers in the Velodrome was essential to determine the layout and minimise clashes.

39 Sections through the seating tier and plenum illustrating different ventilation modes.

40 Daylighting simulation was used to determine the optimal layout of rooflights to provide even light on the track without glare.

A clear brief, an enlightened client willing to commission an integrated team from the outset and good team synergy were key determinants of the Velodrome's final form. Each team member was willing to work beyond their own remit to navigate the complexities of a multi-headed client. Early involvement of a committed contractor and a longer than usual gestation period meant that most detail design issues and specification choices could be largely resolved before the project went on site.

The Velodrome has all the makings of a memorable building that will become a destination in the northern part of the Park. Certain to be appreciated by cyclists, its recognisable form will also serve as a point of orientation for casual Park users and motorists on the adjacent A12. Its programming and that of the surrounding facilities to engage amateur as well as elite cyclists will be critical to its ongoing success.

KEY POINTS
Integrated design
Natural ventilation and daylight reduce loads
A taut 'shrink-wrapped envelope' reduces internal volume
Heavily insulated external envelope
Lightweight roof structure reduces embodied energy
Early contractor engagement
Working beyond one's remit

43 View of the Velodrome in the newly landscaped Park. Its distinctive roof form will be easily identifiable in the Olympic Park and from the adjacent A12 dual-carriage way.

Handball Arena

The Handball Arena is a top-lit arena with retractable seating that increases its flexibility to accommodate different Games and legacy uses. The final building differs little from the original competition scheme and easily met BREEAM Excellent because it is a compact well-insulated building with high recycled content in both its copper cladding and concrete.

The architects refer to the Handball Arena as a jewel box. It has a solid, robust exterior that sparkles inside. A single-minded design, it is driven by efficiency and ease of delivery. It is the simplest of forms, a top-lit rectangular box. A solid copper-clad envelope floats over a glazed entry level that opens on to a striking red concourse around all four sides of the building. Located near the western entrance to the Park, it is easily reached on foot from Hackney Wick rail station and is about a 15-minute walk from Stratford to the east.

The Handball Arena's capacity was planned with long-term community uses in mind. It ranges up to 6,000 for the Handball competition and down to 3,000 to increase the size of the field of play during legacy. During the Olympic Games, the building will host Handball only through the quarter-finals; the semi-finals and final will relocate to the larger Basketball Arena (see pp. 132–141). It will also host the fencing element of the Modern Pentathlon. During the Paralympic Games, it will be the venue for the Goalball competition. The interior volume of the Arena was established by overlaying the fields of play for the various sports taking place during the Games with layouts for legacy sports such as basketball, badminton, volleyball and handball. A fitness club and café also form part of the long-term brief, though no end user had been identified at design stage.

'The building was designed for legacy and dressed for the Games rather than the other way around. At times, it was quite challenging to push people's mindsets to understand this.'

STUART FRASER, MAKE

The Olympic Park Loop Road and numerous underground constraints, including the tunnel for the Channel Tunnel Rail Link and a water main, determined the Handball Arena's precise location on the site. Like the other venues on the Park, the need to keep excavation to a minimum meant that extensive site regrading was required to ground the building and create a welcoming approach. A plaza that opens onto the main concourse will be retained after the Games for use during large events, and a secondary entrance that can be easily

ENVIRONMENTAL PROFILE

BREEAM: Excellent

Predicted CO$_2$ emissions reduction beyond Part L 2006: 20%

Predicted reduction in potable water consumption: 59.5%

Recycled content (proportion of secondary materials as percentage of value): 23%

Recycled aggregate (proportion of secondary materials as percentage of mass): 27%

Sustainable transport (delivery of materials by rail/water): 70%

U-values

walls: 0.29 W/m^{2}K

roof: 0.18 W/m^{2}K

floor: 0.25 W/m^{2}K

glazing: 1.8 W/m^{2}K

Airtightness: 2.9m3/(h.m^2) @ 50 Pa

MATERIALS

Main materials: Concrete, steel, copper

Materials with recycled content: copper cladding, 100% stent in concrete pilings

Innovative materials, products, technologies or approaches: extensive use of sun pipes, provision of flexible wheelchair viewing positions

44 The Handball Arena's copper cladding has 65 per cent recycled content. The remaining primary content from Chile had to meet the ODA's requirements for responsible sourcing. This meant that every copper roll was stamped and documented.

supervised by a small staff will operate on a daily basis. This entrance forms part of the back of house area during the Games.

The expansion of the legacy use from a multi-sport venue to include concerts required the Arena to meet strict acoustical criteria for breakout sound. This did not prove overly onerous because the acoustic requirements for Goalball, a sport for the visually impaired that uses a ball with bells inside, necessitate high levels of acoustic isolation to keep sound out. A sinusoidal profile to the upper tier was introduced to further break up sound inside the venue.

DESIGN DEVELOPMENT

A simple structure of standard trusses, a compact form with a minimum number of apertures, high levels of insulation and recessed glazing all contribute to an efficient design. In terms of sustainability, three elements of the Handball Arena's design are worth noting: its retractable seating, the use of sunpipes to provide natural light and the choice of copper for the cladding.

MAKE, the architects, had not previously used retractable seating, but found numerous products on the market and noted increasing use of such systems, particularly in higher

45 Exploded view of the Handball Arena, illustrating placement of sunpipes.

46 Interior corner of the Handball Arena showing the mid-level daylit entry concourse beyond.

47 Interior view with retractable seating that increases the flexibility of the Handball Arena for a wide range of events.

45

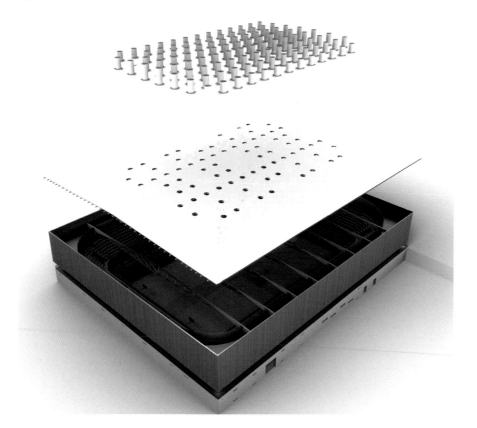

education buildings and academies. An off-the-shelf system that retracts by pushing a button was selected for ease of operation and to minimise risk. The retractable seating determined the section design of the building, because all spectators, including any wheelchair users, enter at mid-level above the point where the seating retracts. Wheelchair positions are distributed all the way around the bowl to offer a variety of viewing angles. Adjacent seats can be interchanged to provide any number of seats next to a wheelchair position, depending on the audience requirements for a particular event. BOH (back of house) areas are below and the lower part of the seating bowl is buried into the ground.

Sunpipes offer a lightweight affordable alternative to other forms of rooflights, one that the architects had successfully used on a previous project. Some 88 1.5m-diameter sunpipes are carefully positioned to cast even light over the field of play. The sunpipes are 4.5m deep with a mirror-polished metal interior finish, and they are self-cleaning which means that access to the roof is not required for maintenance. According to calculations by Arup, they are predicted to reduce overall lighting demand in the Arena by 40 per cent. The sunpipes are

48 Interior view of Handball Arena. The ceiling is fitted with 88 sunpipes that bring daylight onto the fields of play, reducing lighting demand by 40 per cent compared to a blacked out venue.

fitted with 'butterfly' flaps so they can be blacked out as necessary to accommodate the requirements of high-definition television during the Games.

Royal College of Art students undertook computer studies to develop a pattern for the multi-coloured seating that together with the sunpipes enlivens the Arena's interior. A random pattern was eventually selected because it worked best when the seats were fully or partially retracted. ODA Principal Access Officer Margaret Hickish notes that the use of different coloured seats is a useful orienting device for the visually impaired.

Numerous approaches to cladding the 3,000m² exterior of the building were explored, including multi-coloured panels in a variety of patterns. The final selection of copper, chosen for its rich visual qualities, its durability, and for environmental reasons, enhances the Handball Arena's simple exterior with an ever-changing play of light. Made in Germany, the cladding contains over 65 per cent recycled content, sourced from scraps from the manufacturer's production process and from copper scrap merchants. The remaining primary material from Minera Escondida mine in Chile was subject to the ODA's responsible sourcing code. Individually stamped by number, every copper roll could be cross-referenced to its delivery note and source. This was a relatively new process, implemented only for the second time by the manufacturer to meet the ODA's requirements. The cladding can be entirely recycled.

To reduce potable water consumption, the Handball Arena's 75m x 120m rectangular roof is used in its entirety for rainwater harvesting. Four tanks, located at the corners of the building, store the water used for flushing of toilets. In combination with use of water-efficient fittings, these measures are predicted to reduce potable water demand by almost 60%.

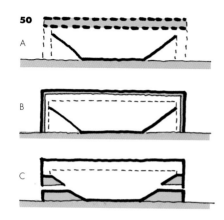

49 Concealed roof plant conditions air via plenums below the seating tiers.

50 Design process sketches illustrate that a compact building delivers value for money: a. Clear span with efficient structure. b. Minimal internal volume. c. Back of house uses accommodated below seating tier.

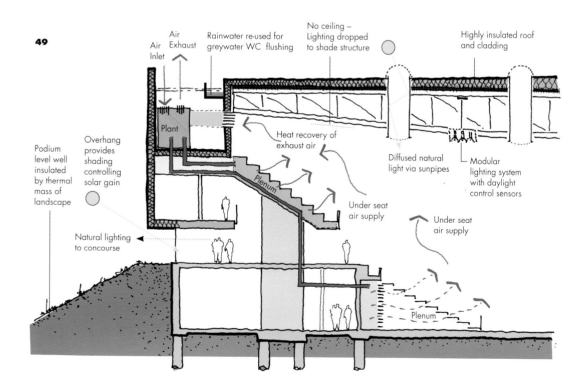

51

Legacy field of play   Games field of play   Modern Pentathlon – fencing field of play   Handball and Goalball field of play

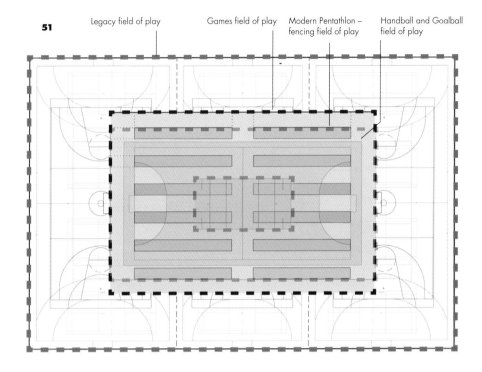

52

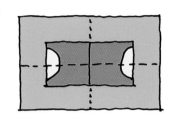

A. Determine field of play for Games and legacy sports

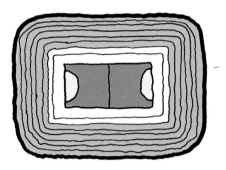

B. Design compact seating bowl without compromising sight lines

KEEP IT SIMPLE

MAKE's approach to the Handball Arena was to design a simple, elegant building sufficiently flexible to accommodate multiple community uses in the future. The copper cladding will age well within the Park's natural setting, and the strong use of colour inside enlivens the interior. Like the Velodrome, the building benefited from a relatively clear vision for its legacy use that helped shape the design.

Both Hopkins and MAKE, with its ex-Foster lineage, are longstanding practitioners of Britain's high-tech tradition, noted for a modernist aesthetic of well-crafted buildings based on efficient structural and environmental design. Responding to London 2012's sustainable design agenda, both practices have delivered permanent venues within the Olympic Park that synthesise environmental concerns with quality architecture.

KEY POINTS

Compact form with minimal junctions (facilitates airtightness)
Retractable seating increases flexibility
Sunpipes provide natural light – low-cost and low-risk solution
Copper cladding – recycled and recyclable

51 The Arena's size was determined by overlaying the fields of play for the sports that are to be played in the building during the Olympic and Paralympic Games – Handball, Goalball, and Modern Pentathlon – fencing – with a range of amateur sports that are likely to be played in the Arena when it is converted for community sports use in legacy.

52 Design process sketches illustrate that a compact building delivers value for money:
a. Fields of play for Games and legacy.
b. Compact seating bowl.

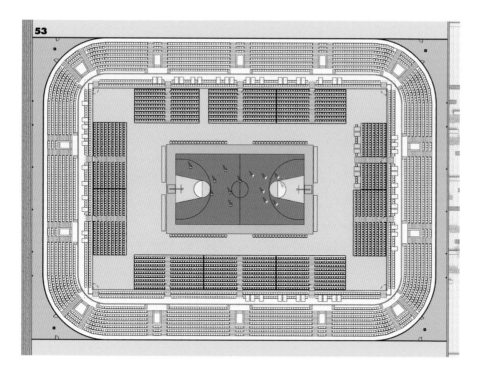

53 Legacy plan of Handball Arena with 7,000 capacity for an event.

54 Legacy plan of Handball Arena with seating retracted reduces Games-time capacity to 3,000 and increases fields of play.

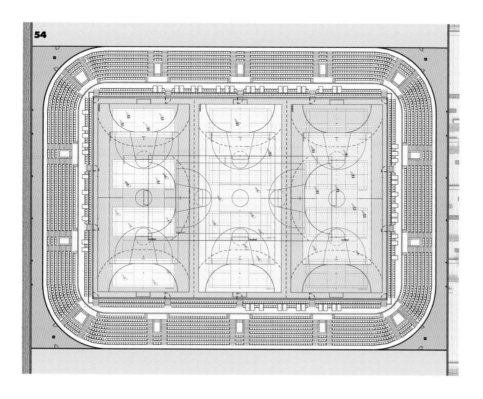

Eton Manor

Eton Manor is the most complex Games venue in terms of its radically changing programme: during the Games it provides an Aquatics training centre and a venue for Wheelchair Tennis; post-Games it becomes a community sports facility surrounded by allotments. Despite its shifting use, the scheme for the Games minimises the use of temporary structures.

The venue is a catalyst for future development of the Olympic Park. Rather than seeking a temporary solution to the provision of facilities for London 2012, it is envisioned as a permanent structure that is an 'urban sticking plaster'. The site typifies all the discontinuities in the existing fabric that characterise the Olympic Park precinct. Surrounded by roads on three sides and the river to the west, the area is cut off from the Olympic Park by the A12.

An important aspect of Stanton Williams' approach to masterplanning Eton Manor was extensive regrading and landscaping of the site to better integrate it with the surrounding area and create appealing pedestrian paths to the Olympic Park from the north. The ground level of the entire site was raised by 2.5m using fill from the Olympic Park, a mound of earth was created to screen the A12 to the south and along the western Hackney Marsh boundary, a raised concourse was created that forms an enclosure to the Hockey Centre after the Games.

During the Olympic and Paralympic Games, Eton Manor is an Aquatics training venue, housing three 50m temporary swimming pools, as well as temporary pools for Synchronised Swimming and Water Polo. During the Paralympic Games, it will also host the Wheelchair Tennis competitions with temporary capacity for 10,500 spectators. After the Games, the permanent facilities are transformed into a variety of community sporting facilities, including the Hockey Centre that reuses the pitches from the London 2012 Hockey Centre, a tennis centre and five-a-side football pitches. Like the Velodrome and the White Water Centre, Eton Manor will be operated by LVRPA and consultation with a designated end user facilitated the design process even though the final brief for the building's operation was not fully defined.

The masterplanning of the site was largely influenced by the early proposal for a wind turbine whose location and exclusion zone determined the siting of the venues. Accommodating the various fields of play and the permanent building proved a challenge, and early on Paralympic Archery was relocated to The Royal Artillery Barracks. Special

ENVIRONMENTAL PROFILE

BREEAM: Excellent

Predicted CO$_2$ emissions reduction beyond Part L 2006: 15%

Predicted reduction in potable water consumption: 55% (not including hockey pitch irrigation)

Recycled content (proportion of secondary materials as percentage of value): 20% (sports complex) and 33% (civils) – (forecast)

Recycled aggregate (proportion of secondary materials as percentage of mass): 74% (sports complex and civils) – (forecast)

U-values (Stage D)

external wall: 0.35 W/m2K

roof: 0.25 W/m2K

floor: 0.25 W/m2K

external glazing (inc. frames): 1.56 W/m2K

MATERIALS

Main materials: concrete, timber

Materials with recycled content: in situ concrete

Innovative materials, products, technologies and approaches: Large single span glulam beams, off-site timber cassette construction

55 Games aerial visualisation showing extent of overlay at Eton Manor venue and concourse bridge spanning the A12 and Ruckholt Road.

authorisation from the IOC was required to orientate certain fields of play 9° off the required north–south axis in order to fit everything on the site and minimise the amount of transformation that would have to take place after the Games. To this same end, the platforms for the legacy fields of play are constructed below the temporary elements required for the Games.

The permanent building that houses the tennis courts anchors the site. Discussions about future-proofing at early design stage led to a flexible rectilinear building rather than an A-framed structure common for sports halls – even though more costly – because a mezzanine could be introduced to accommodate additional activities if required at a later date.

'The ODA environmental objectives were fantastic. In every project, we try to lock them in with a client through early discussion of standards and how we would like to better them. [On the Eton Manor scheme,] there was no budging and no possibility that environmental measures would be value-engineered out.'

RAWDEN PETTITT, ASSOCIATE, STANTON WILLIAMS ARCHITECTS

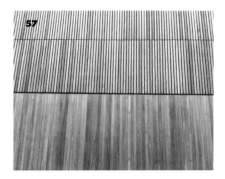

56 Legacy aerial visualisation showing the Eton Manor legacy sports complex with community building, hockey and tennis facilities and bridges over the roads reduced in size after the Games.

57 Detail photograph of the Western red Cedar cladding on the Eton Manor community sports building.

1. Sports Centre Complex – 4 indoor tennis courts / Changing / Hospitality

2. Main Hockey Stadium – 3000 spectators

3. 6 external tennis courts

4. Hockey pitch – no permanent spectator facilities

5. Allotments

6. 5-a-side football

7. Mountain Bike trail

8. Utilities enclosure

9. Public meadow and entrance plaza with relocated war memorial

10. Car park

11. Vehicle entrance

12. Pedestrian entrance to Olympic Park

13. Bridge link to East Marshes over Ruckholt Road

14. Bridge link to Velodrome over A12

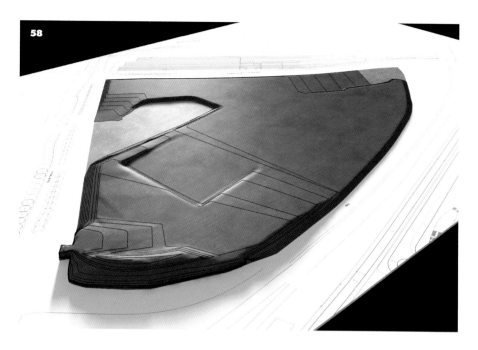

58 Topographical study showing mounding of Eton Manor site perimeter to screen roads and parking areas. All fill on the site came from the Olympic Park.

59 Temporary Wheelchair Tennis courts for the Games with the Velodrome beyond.

60

Primarily serviced by natural ventilation, the building uses in situ concrete for thermal mass. A single span glulam structure is enclosed with prefabricated timber cassettes on a 1,200mm module with minimal waste. Lightweight linear polycarbonate skylights allow an even distribution of daylight; other glazing is carefully located for light and views and provided with solar shading where required.

The use of PVs was ruled out due to cost and the additional structure required. To meet the biodiversity provision, the lower block of the tennis building has a brown roof and bird boxes are fixed to the north-facing upstands of the skylights. No provision was made for bats due to the proposed wind turbine. A new area for allotments replaces the much-loved allotments previously on the site.

The regrading and landscaping of the site are a first step towards linking the Eton Manor site with adjacent streets and over the A12 to the Olympic Park. The urban design approach involved breaking down what was previously an island site surrounded by a 3m-high wall to create permanent pedestrian paths to the Olympic Park. A new garden reinstates a pre-existing war memorial from the Eton Manor Boys' Club, which previously occupied the site, using bricks reclaimed from the site's perimeter wall in the paving. Disparate temporary

60 Construction photograph of the interior of the tennis hall at Eton Manor, built with timber glulam beams and timber cassettes. Rooflights bring natural light onto the courts, reducing lighting loads.

61 Visualisation of multi-purpose room at Eton Manor with exposed concrete ceiling to benefit from thermal mass.

venues were arranged to suit this long-term plan, and even when the proposed wind turbine was eliminated, the urban design moves and basic site organisation remained unchanged. The focus of the site is the new sports venue, a flexible building with tennis and five-a-side Football facilities, which, if well managed, could provide the hub of activity needed to attract nearby residents to Eton Manor and on into the Park.

KEY POINTS

Future-proofing building to be flexible for multiple uses
Extensive regrading and re-landscaping of site with Olympic Park fill to create 'gateway' from the north
Permanent venue anchor site

Basketball Arena

The Basketball Arena is one of the largest temporary venues ever erected for any Olympic and Paralympic Games. With a capacity of 12,000, it is the fourth biggest venue at the Olympic Park, after the Olympic Stadium, the Aquatics Centre and the temporary Hockey Centre. The design team set out to create a state-of-the-art temporary building. Though the aspirations were tempered by the realities of programme and budget, many useful lessons emerge from the design process.

With a façade very close in size to the Tate Modern, the bulk of the Basketball Arena looms large and is clearly visible from many vantage points in the Olympic Park. As host to the Handball finals as well as Basketball, the venue was sized to Handball's larger field of play. It also serves as a staging area for athletes during the Opening and Closing Ceremonies and will host Wheelchair Rugby and Wheelchair Basketball during the Paralympic Games. Sited on high ground at the north end of the Park near the Velodrome, it measures 25m at the eaves, the equivalent of a 10-storey building. Architectural presence was therefore extremely important. Demands for back of house (BOH) access mean that the Arena is a one-sided venue, and its siting in relationship to the Velodrome was another key consideration. How the building might be reused after the Games, in whole or in part, was a driver in the design from the outset.

A STATE-OF-THE-ART TEMPORARY BUILDING

Reuse was considered from a variety of angles by Wilkinson Eyre Architects and the team. The building could be packed up in its entirety and sent to another Olympic and Paralympic Games; it could be subdivided into, for example, several sports halls across the UK or reconfigured using its component parts to create an entirely different form. Or it could be dismantled with individual elements reused or recycled. The first two approaches proved to not be viable because designing in future flexibility increases costs. To withstand repeated future use, each component has to be more robust. Budget constraints ruled out the possibility of spending more upfront to enable speculative reuse scenarios. So the mantra for the project became design for dismantling. The objective was to develop an economical solution for structure, seating and cladding that would still provide elegance and visual drama for spectators for the building's short life during the Games.

Because every element of the building – including the foundations – had to be removed after the Games, each component was reduced to an absolute minimum. Unlike the permanent venues that use deep piles to penetrate the 10m of fill that covers most of the Park, the Basketball Arena had to touch the ground lightly. The sourcing of components

ENVIRONMENTAL PROFILE

BREEAM: N/A

Predicted CO² emissions reduction beyond Part L 2006: N/A

Predicted reduction in potable water consumption: 51%

Recycled content (proportion of secondary materials as percentage of value): 29.8%

Recycled aggregate (proportion of secondary materials as percentage of mass): 28%

Sustainable transport (delivery of materials by rail/water): 78%

U-values: N/A

MATERIALS

Main materials: Steel, concrete, phthalate-free PVC

Materials with recycled content: Fill material with recycled glass, seating, PVC

Innovative materials, products, technologies or approaches: Take-back scheme for PVC, procurement in separate packages transferring responsibility for reuse to individual contractors

62 Detail of the Basketball Arena's folded phthalate-free PVC cladding.

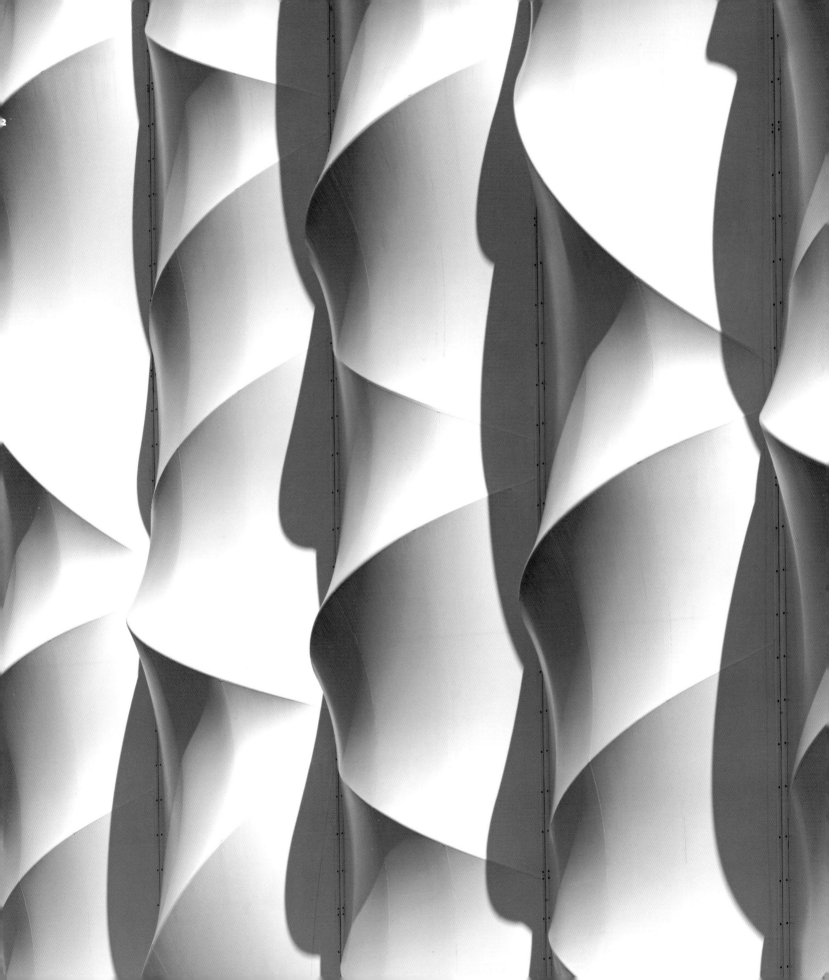

from temporary events specialists was explored. This proved feasible for the seating tiers, but the size of the project meant that there were no precedents for the Arena's structure or envelope that could be hired off the shelf.

DESIGN DEVELOPMENT

For the Arena's structure, the design team developed a matrix of 17 generic options that were rated against a range of variables, including demountability, potential reuse and embodied energy. Two options, a portal frame and a dome, were developed through Stage C. The dome had numerous advantages – striking visual appearance and ability to accommodate all BOH functions in the ancillary space – but was eventually rejected on cost grounds, largely due to its higher risk factor compared to a conventional portal frame.

Foundations were kept to a minimum. Dynamic thumping was used to compact the ground, and a slab was laid only under the field of play. Stone footings were vibrated into the ground to support the footings for the portal frame, and steel sheets, which could be easily removed after the Games, were driven into the ground to resist the lateral thrust of the portal arches. A scaffold seating system proved most suitable, and modifications were minimised so that it could be easily returned to the marketplace. The seating, completely independent of the frame and cladding, sits on precast concrete pads.

63 Cutaway section view of the Arena illustrates how individual components can be easily dismantled. Use of off-the-shelf or hired components maximises the opportunities for reuse and recycling after the Games. Only the cladding is bespoke and a take-back clause was negotiated with the contractor.

64 Aerial view of the temporary 12,000-capacity Basketball Arena.

65 Back of house corridor between modular accommodation units at the Basketball Arena. These will go back into the hire market after the Games.

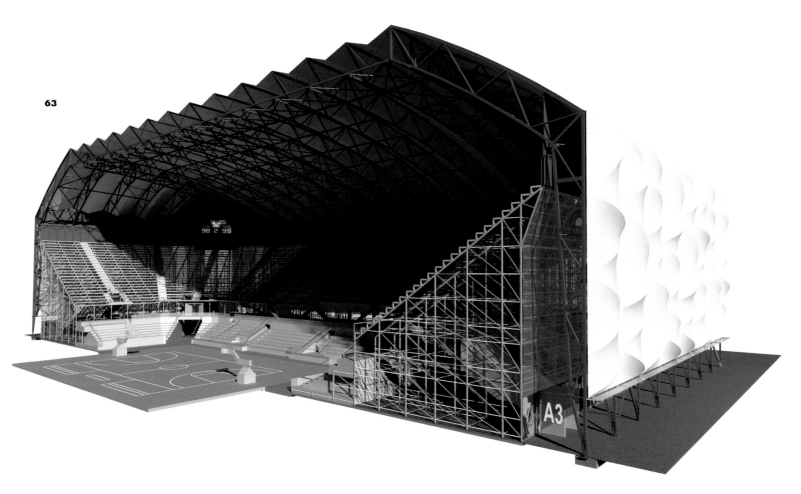

63

‘We were driven very very hard. Sustainability was constantly on the agenda and we were challenged at every step of the way to prove that what we were doing had been fully assessed in terms of its environmental impact.’

NICK LING, SKM CONSULTING (STRUCTURAL ENGINEER)

To keep the structure to a minimum, movement up to 200 mm in high winds was deemed acceptable. The venue has no heating, and the mechanical and electrical (M&E) plant for cooling is hired for the duration of the Games only. The uninsulated single skin cladding is compensated for by increasing the number of AHUs required for the short duration of the Games. Minimal concern was given to M&E systems because they are hired in for a short time. BOH functions for the Basketball Arena and the Velodrome are located in a separate building, which incorporated both recycled plasterboard and prefabricated toilet pods. The ODA's target for recycled content was primarily met through a combination of recycled glass beads in the fill material under the building and recycled seating. Because black seats are more easily recycled, a minimum of 70 per cent black seats were provided.

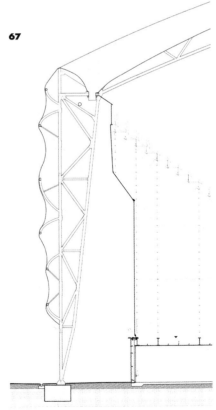

66 View of entrance zone and minimal steel structure behind single skin PVC cladding.

67 Section through the external envelope of the Basketball Arena. A conventional steel portal frame supports a secondary structure of radial steel tubes that in turn supports the PVC membrane.

68 Exploded axonometric of Basketball Arena components, illustrating its minimal use of materials, use of standard components and demountability: single skin membrane cladding, portal frame steelwork, hired seating system, plenum, and shallow foundations.

66

67

68

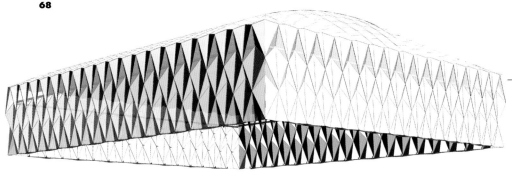

Membrane cladding (single skin)

Reduces need for second skin

No insulation – sound, thermal etc.

Membrane can be re-ground into pellets for re-use.

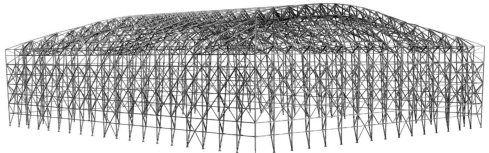

Portal frame steelwork

High potential for re-use/recyclability

Serviceability considered for the short term where possible to avoid extra stiffening material

Corrosion protection avoided where steel not needed longer than 2 years

Seating system and sports equipment

Buy back deal with suppliers for continued use in the rental market

Precast concrete footing to be used complete with seating system

Lighting & Scoreboards hired out

Field of Play (FOP) & Equipment hired out

Plenum

Polycarbonate can be ground down and re-extruded

Insulation properties provided by twinwall polycarbonate reduces cooling load

AHU's hired out for test events and Games

Fresh air supply can be used if exterior air temperature drops below 18C

Transfer structure and foundations

Bespoke steelwork may be reused by seating supplier

Shallow foundations as opposed to piling

Sheet piles extracted and returned to contractor

Field of play slab is ground bearing – no deep foundations

In situ concrete easily extracted, crushed and reused

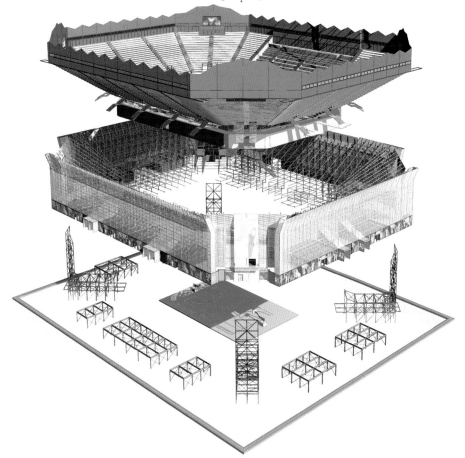

THE CLADDING – ENHANCING 'PLAIN VANILLA'

Once the dome design was put on hold, it became clear that a portal frame design would result in an enormous rectangular volume. At this point, the baseline scheme was dubbed 'plain vanilla', and a consensus emerged that the façade needed to be enhanced. A range of cladding materials, including glazing, timber and metals, was explored. A detail design study looked at both timber and folded PVC. With the input of the Creative Design Group, the transfer of digital images onto a framework of timber slats whose size and density could be varied was used to create both abstract and figurative patterns on the façade.

69 Comparison matrix of cladding options. Sustainability considerations include thermal properties, demountability, potential reuse and recyclability.

70 A take-back clause was negotiated with the supplier of the Basketball Arena's PVC cladding to ensure that it would be recycled in the event that an alternate use for the building could not be identified.

69

Criteria	Weighting	Metal (Sandwich e.g. deck, insulation & top sheet)	Metal (Single skin e.g. profiled sheeting only)	Single ply membranes (e.g. Sarnafil on timber / steel dec)	Structural membrane (Short span continuous e.g. PVC coated polyester)	Structural membrane (Long span continuous e.g. PVC coated polyester)	Structural membrane (Discrete e.g. ETFE cushions)	Timber (Plank system)	Plastics (Single sheet e.g. polycarbonate or GRP profiled sheets)	Plastics (Discrete light openings e.g. polycarbonate or GRPpanels)	Glazing (Continuous)
Weight of cladding (kg/m2)		20	2.5	~0.2	0.75	1	5	25	~2.5	~10	35
Arrangement of support		~2>6m c/c	~2m c/c	~2>6m c/c	~2>6m c/c	Cable supported, (>20m)	~2>5m c/c	~1m c/c	~1.5m c/c	~1.5m c/c	~2m c/c
Weight of secondary support (kg/m2)		~0>5	~5	~0>5	N/A	N/A	N/A	~5	~15	~15	~15
Cost of cladding (£/m2) • Material		30>33	10>15	21>28	50 TBC	55	180	TBA	26>35	25>40	TBA
• Material + Installation		60>65	20>30	60>80	80 TBC	160	280	TBA	~35>45	35>50	TBA
Translucency		No	No	No	Medium	Medium	Medium > High	No	Medium > High	Medium > High	Medium > High
Thermal properties • Insulative		Very good	Poor	Good	Poor	Poor	Average	Very good	Poor	Poor	Poor
• Solar gain		No	No	No	Little	Little	Poor	No	Poor	Poor	Poor
Acoustic issues: • Reverberation		Good	Poor	Average	Poor	Poor with possible focusing effects	Poor	Good	Poor	Poor	Poor
• Rain drumming		Good	Poor	Average	Poor	Poor	Good	Average	Poor	Poor	Average
Buildability		Very good	Good	Good	Excellent	Exellent	Good	Average	Poor	Poor	Good
Demountability		Poor	Good	Average	Excellent	Exellent	Good	Poor	Average	Average	Good
Ceiling required		No	No	No	No	No	No	Likely	No	No	No
Sustainability Issues: • Re-use / relocatable		Standing seam and clips only	Yes	No	Yes	No	No	No	No	No	Partially
• Recyclability		Yes	Yes	Yes	Yes	Yes	Yes	No	Yes	Yes	Yes
• Renewable		No	No	No	No	No	No	Yes	No	No	Yes
Compatibility with primary structure • Planar roof surface (8, 9, 11a, 11b, 11c, 12)		Yes	Yes	Yes	Yes	N/A	Yes	No	Yes	Yes	Yes
• Singly curved roof surface or similar (1a, 2a, 2b, 4a, 4b)		Yes	Yes	No	Yes	N/A	Yes	Part	Faceted	Faceted	Yes/Faceted
• Significant doubly curved roof surface (1b, 3)		No	No	No	Yes	N/A	Yes	Part	No	Faceted	Faceted
• Other (5, 6, 7, 10)		N/A	N/A	N/A	Limited span	Yes	N/A	N/A	N/A	N/A	N/A
Total score (unweighted)		**49**	**50**	**46**	**52**	**40**	**50**	**48**	**39**	**40**	**48**
Total score (weighted)		**127**	**132**	**116**	**131**	**91**	**115**	**119**	**102**	**102**	**123**

1   2   3   4   5

70

71

Meanwhile, the ODA was in the process of negotiating a Park-wide strategy for PVC. PVC was selected as the preferred option, and a diamond pattern was agreed as the compliant scheme for the tender, but contractors were asked to come forward with alternatives. The winning supplier proposed a steel subframe with radial arches to articulate the PVC. The design calls for the envelope to be backlit with elaborate programmable lighting effects. In the end, the cost of the timber and the lighting are roughly comparable.

PROCUREMENT
The Basketball Arena was the first temporary venue to be procured, and a carrot and stick approach set the standard for procurement of all temporary structures for the Games. The Arena design was divided into six packages that were procured separately. The onus for reuse of the individual elements was transferred to each subcontractor: substructure and civils, seating bowl, envelope, BOH, M&E and general building. An unanticipated result of this approach was that the architects found themselves coordinating the interface between packages, such as how to attach plasterboard for the BOH areas to the seating without damaging it so that it could be returned to the hire market.

The Basketball Arena illustrates the challenge of trailblazing sustainable design when a supply chain is not in place to respond. The final building does not fully reflect the multitude of typologies and materials that were explored during the design process. The underlying premise of a temporary venue – to avoid leaving behind an under-used white elephant after the Games, is a valid one. The overarching objectives of keeping costs and risk down dictated the use of solutions readily available in the marketplace. Steel portal frames are more widespread than timber domes.

The key driver – design for dismantling – meant that each element of the building had to be self-standing. This contrasts markedly with the Velodrome where each design element is fully integrated into a whole. Faced with limitations of budget and programme, it is logical that the ODA opted to invest more in permanent venues than in temporary ones.

KEY POINTS
Design for dismantling – ease of deconstruction
Maximum use of hireable and standard components
Minimum bespoke alteration of standard components
Procurement in separate packages
Design for future flexibility costs more

71 Interior view of the Basketball Arena with the hired scaffold seating system that will be returned to the hire market after the Games

72 The Arena seating has 70 per cent recycled content from reused stadia seating. As can be seen in image 71, the majority of the seating is black, because it is the easiest colour to create from recycled seating. All seating goes back into the hire market.

73 The scaffold seating is exposed below to make it apparent that it is a temporary system. The 3m x 3m grid of the seating scaffold is supported on individual steel base plates that sit on compacted ground and hence eliminate the need for concrete foundations.

74 (Overleaf) The 25m-high Basketball Arena sits on high ground and is visible from many vantage points in the Park. Although it is a temporary structure, strong visual presence was a key design consideration.

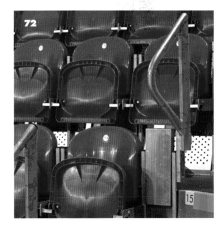

Water Polo Arena

Located on a prominent site facing the Aquatics Centre at the Stratford gateway to the Olympic Park, the Water Polo Arena's main challenge is effectively creating a dramatic presence for the Olympic Games with a temporary structure. Given the venue's short duration, the main criteria for selection of materials became reuse and recyclability, rather than embodied or operational energy. All of the building's primary components – structure, envelope and seating – are either hired or recyclable.

This London 2012 Arena is the first bespoke Water Polo venue for an Olympic Games. Awkward site access, which requires crossing the main entrance bridge from Stratford and looping back across another bridge to arrive at the main entrance, posed a considerable design challenge, as did the fact that one side of the pool is occupied by a large referees' table that obstructs spectator views. In response, David Morley Architects proposed an asymmetrical scheme that allows unobstructed views of the Olympic Stadium over the low end of the building and enables the majority of spectators to be seated to one side of the pool opposite the referees' table to get the best views. The 25m-high end of the wedge forms the entrance, while the low end covers the training pool, which requires only a 6m clearance. Cladding the structure in translucent PVC pillows, the architects envisioned the wedge-shaped building as a temporary 'splash' created by the Aquatics Centre. Crossing the bridge into the Park from Stratford, visitors will overlook the billowing roof.

DESIGN DEVELOPMENT

The building takes advantage of a 3m level change between the bridge level and the site to minimise excavation of contaminated soil. Only 1m of fill had to be excavated to accommodate the pools, which are 2m-deep prefabricated tanks made of steel panels with a phthalate-free PVC liner. The building sits on screwpile foundations that are fixed through the marker layer for contaminated soil and can be removed and reused after the Games.

A rectangular building plan maximises the use of off-the-shelf structural elements and seating stands available directly from the hire market. These are installed without bespoke modifications, which means they can be easily returned to the supply chain after the Games. The structure is comprised of pre-existing truss components of varying height on a 12m centre. The fact that the design team worked with temporary suppliers from concept stage influenced the design of the rectilinear building, which accommodates 5,000 seats in straight rows with no corners. As with some of the other London 2012 venues, the seating supplier opted to renew its stock and the seats supplied for the Water Polo Arena are new and will be reused in other events after the Games.

75 Water Polo Arena. Construction view, showing recyclable PVC cushions spanning off-the-shelf steel trusses.

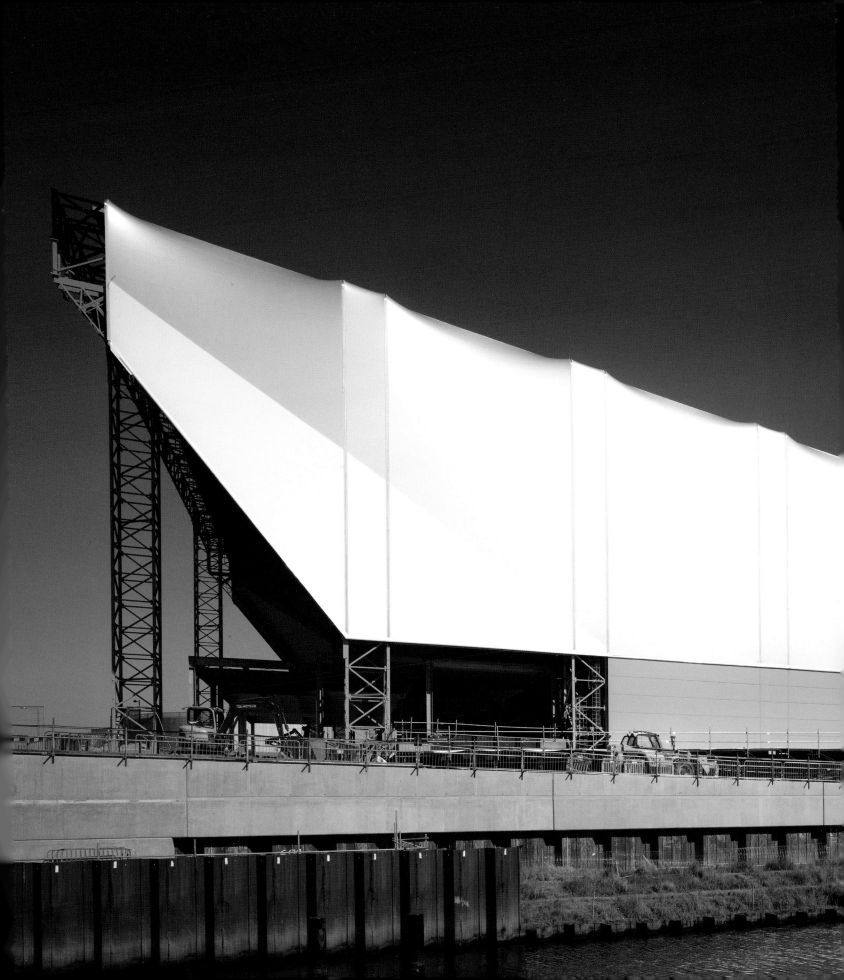

'The flexibility to work with the supply chain before the design was frozen meant that we could look at anything impacting sustainability and adapt the design to suit what was available in the marketplace rather than force suppliers into a bespoke solution which could not be reused.'

DAVID MORLEY, ARCHITECT

Inflatable PVC cushions, an alternative to Ethylene tetrafluoroethylene (ETFE) that creases and is therefore difficult to reuse, form both cladding and structural enclosure for the roof and walls. The cushions themselves span up to 54m, eliminating the need for another secondary structure. The cushions can be rolled and removed after use and will be taken back by manufacturer Ferrari for either recycling or reuse.

The environmental strategy for the Arena parallels the approach of the permanent venues in creating a targeted zone of conditioned air around the pool deck using mechanical plant, while the seating stands are naturally ventilated. The inflated PVC cushions provide an insulated layer that helps control condensation.

76 Section showing Water Polo Arena structure, cladding, seating stands and pools.

77 Exploded axonometric explaining the Water Polo Arena as a kit of parts that can be easily demountable after the Games.

76

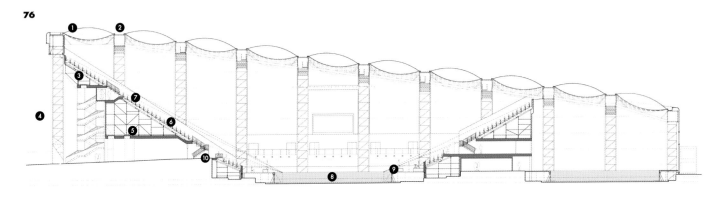

1. 10m x 50m inflated phthalate-free PVC membrane, self-supporting

2. Off-the-shelf trusses (100% returned to supply chain after Games)

3. Upper plenum with airtight wrap

4. Motorised louvres

5. Lower plenum with air-tight wrap

6. Seat risers perforated for natural ventilation

7. 80% black seats with 100% recycled plastic content

8. Pools from laminated stainless panels which can be adapted for reuse in other pools

9. Pool surround decking demountable

10. Level wheelchair access

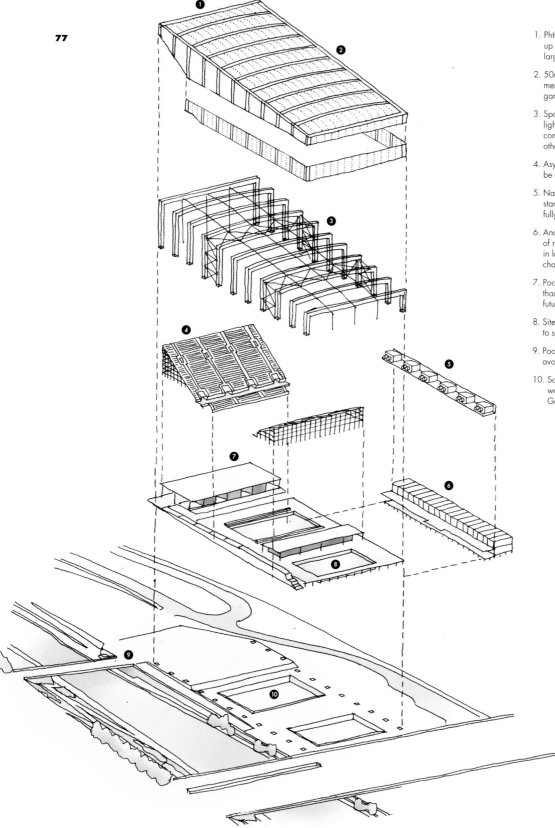

1. Phthalate free PVC envelope can be easily folded up without creasing making it easy to bring to site in large panels and then to re-use after the Games

2. 50m x 10m air inflated phthalate free PVC roof membrane is self-supporting between trusses/lighting gantries at 12m centres

3. Spans are limited to 50m allowing the trusses/ lighting gantries to be assembled from off the shelf components 60% of which have been pre-used on other buildings

4. Asymmetrical seating bowl allows C90 sightlines to be achieved with standard riser heights.

5. Natural ventilation strategy for the main spectator stand reduces need for plant by 50% compared to a fully mechanical solution

6. Ancillary accommodation comes as a 2-storey stack of rented modular buildings which can be brought in late in the programme and returned to the supply chain after the Games

7. Pools are made from laminated stainless steel panels than can be re-formed into different pool sizes for future use in schools or other venues

8. Site ground levels are exploited to allow level access to seating stands

9. Pools are built up from above the marker layer to avoid disturbing contaminated ground

10. Screw pile foundations and sheet piling retaining walls can be easily extracted and re-used after the Games

Fabric	Description	Possible Suppliers	Structural Comments	Blackout Option	Lifespan/ Durability	Reuse	Recycling	Insulation	Acoustic performance	Condensation risk	Anticipated Costs
PVC	Polyester Fibre with PVC Coating	Ferrari Versiedag	PVC fabric comes in a range of strengths (Type I to V) suitable for tensile structures. Span depends on curvature and type, but up to 25-30m achievable	Yes	Warranties are typically 10-15 years, but can be expected to last 15 to 20 years	Can be taken down and re-erected in exactly the same form a number of times	Material can be taken back and broken down for reuse in lower grade fabric materials	Poor. U-value 6.3W/ m2oK	Poor	High	★
PVC – Phthalate-Free	Polyester Fibre with PVC Coating with Non-Phthalate Plasticiser	Ferrari	Similar performance to normal PVC, however Ferrari have currently only tested up to Type II limiting the tensile capacity available	Yes	Ferrari are providing the same warranties as their equivalent PVC products	As PVC	As PVC	Poor. U-value 6.3W/ m2oK	Poor	High	★
Glass reinforce PTFE	Glass Fibre with PTFE Coating	Ferrari Verseidag Birdair	Similar structural performance to PVC fabrics	Yes	Similar warranties to PVC, but life span is expected to exceed 25 years	Not suited to dismantling and reinstallation since floding fabric can damage fibres	Not currently aware of potential for recycling	Poor	Poor	High	★ ★
Gore Tenara	Expanded PTFE Fibres	Gore	Similar structural performance to PVC/PTFE but only available in strength equivalent to PVC Type II	No – more transparent than typical PVC/PTFE	15 year warranty	Excellent for repeated dismantling and reinstallation in exactly the same form	Gore will accept returned product and we think it can be recycled	Poor	Poor	High	★ ★ ★
Tensotherm	Two layers of glass-reinforced PTFE with a Nanogel fill	Birdair/Cabot Corporation	We expect a similar performance to PTFE	Yes	Would expect membrane to perform as normal PTFE but Nanogel blanket unknown	Not suited to dismantling and reinstallation since folding fabric can damage fibres	Not currently aware of potential for recycling	Good. U-value unknown. Could be as low as 1.0W/ m2oK	Good. Attenuates noise break-in/out and reduces internal reverberation	Very Low	★ ★ ★
ETFE cushion	Two layers of Ethylene Tetrafluore-thylene with air-inflated void between	Architen-Landrell Hightex Vector-Foiltec	Spans typically 3m one-way or 5m two-way so will require a secondary steel frame	Yes	Up to 30 years	Offers potential to be recut and reused	Non-recyclable and non-biodegradable. Not aware of any example of recycling.	Average. U-value 3.5W/ m2oK	Very Poor – acoustically transparent and rain drumming an issue	Low	★ ★
Air inflated PVC membrane	Two layers of Polyester Fibre with PVC Coating with air-inflated void between	Ferrari Versiedag	Will perform similarly to PVC, but inflation introduces curvature which will improve span compared to a flat panel membrane.	Yes	Warranties are typically 10-15 years, but can be expected to last 15 to 20 years	Can be taken down and re-erected in exactly the same form a number of times	Material can be taken back and broken down for reuse in lower grade fabric materials.	Average. I-value 2.7W/ m2oK	Average. Better than single membrane PVC and ETFE. Not as good as Tensotherm.	Low	★ ★

■ Good   ■ Adequate   ■ Poor

A long ribbon of two-storey-high modular structures contains catering and broadcasting facilities and is shared with the Aquatics Centre. Designed to go back into the supply chain after the Games, material choices were carefully scrutinised. Fermacell, a combination of recycled gypsum and cellulose fibres from recycled papers, was used in place of plasterboard. Oversized doors were specified so they could be cut down and reused afterwards, and any laminates specified had to meet the full chain of custody.

PROCUREMENT
To reduce costs and enable maximum recycling and reuse of systems, the Water Polo Arena, like the Basketball Arena, was procured in several different packages. Individual subcontractors were then responsible for 'taking back' particular systems and building components. Within the short life of the London 2012 project, increased understanding about the benefits of engaging early with the supply chain enabled greater innovation in both cladding and seating solutions.

78 Matrix of materials for cladding the Water Polo Arena. Sustainability considerations included insulating value, lifespan and durability, reuse and recyclability.

79 Environmental diagram of the Water Polo Arena explaining the ventilation strategy.

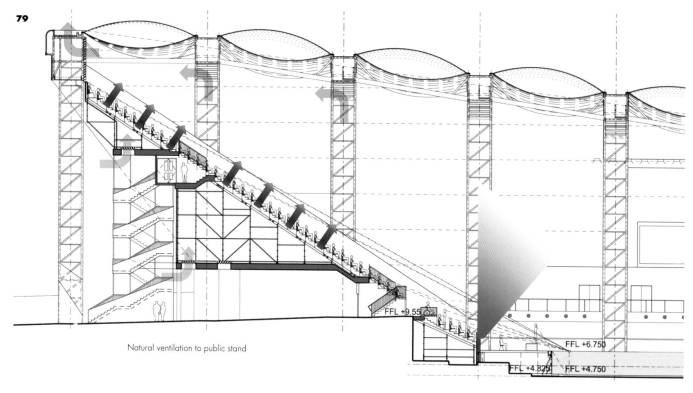

Natural ventilation to public stand

FFL +9.55

FFL +6.750

FFL +4.825   FFL +4.750

Mechanical ventilation to pool surround

The dramatic exterior of the Water Polo Arena proves that temporary design can be both visually appealing and cost-effective. The use of off-the-shelf steel trusses of varying heights combined with a structural PVC cushion make for an elegant lightweight solution. Because phthalate-free PVC was a relatively new product for supplier Ferrari, additional structural and fire testing was performed to confirm the performance criteria of the material. Within the short life of the London 2012 project, lessons learned from the Basketball Arena increased understanding about the benefits of engaging early with the supply chain and enabled greater innovation in both cladding and seating solutions. The result is a striking temporary venue that holds its own at the entrance to the Olympic Park alongside the Olympic Stadium and the Aquatics Centre.

KEY FEATURES

Early supplier engagement informed building design
All components can be reused or recycled
Structural PVC cushions replace secondary structure
Screwpile foundations are easily removable

Lee Valley White Water Centre

The very premise of the Lee Valley White Water Centre (LVWWC) – the creation of artificial white water rapids for an Olympic Canoe Slalom course within a flat river valley landscape on the outskirts of London – is energy-intensive because it relies on electric pumps to move the water. In a departure from previous Games, two water courses have been designed – the competition course and a training course – so that the less energy-hungry practice course can be operated independently when the elite course is not required. A narrow plan facilities building, which consumes a fraction of the energy of the courses, is designed to maximise views, daylight and natural ventilation.

Before and after the Games, the LVWWC will be a permanent canoe, kayak and white water rafting centre that makes these sports available to a wide audience within the greater London region. The point of departure for the LVWWC was the design of an economical and efficient installation that met competition requirements but could also be easily adapted for community use and operated by its end user, the Lee Valley Regional Park Authority.

Canoe Slalom became a regular Olympic sport in 1992, and most venues have been purpose-built artificial courses with water forced through a concrete channel by electric pumps to create the white water conditions required for competition. The artificially pumped course makes Canoe Slalom one of the most intensive consumers of energy per person of any Games event. Over 90 per cent of the energy demand for the LVWWC comes from pumping water to the head of the course, with the remainder for the building and external lighting. The design team recognised early on that a critical design consideration was minimising the operation of the pumps and sizing them appropriately.

ENVIRONMENTAL PROFILE

BREEAM: Very Good

Predicted CO$_2$ emissions reduction beyond Building Regulations Part L 2006: 21%

Predicted reduction in potable water consumption: 45%

Recycled content (proportion of secondary materials as percentage of value): 40%

Recycled aggregate (proportion of secondary materials as percentage of mass): 75%

Sustainable transport: N/A

U-values: N/A

MATERIALS

Main materials: concrete, timber

Materials with recycled content: recycled aggregate in concrete

Reclaimed materials: imported fill for road and pavement sub-bases

Innovative materials, products, technologies or approaches: dividing white water course into two independent loops that could be operated separately, designing to minimal drop in course height

80 A large roof overhang and vertical timber blades in FSC-sourced western red cedar provide adjustable solar shading from the south and west on the main terrace elevation at the Lee Valley White Water Centre in Broxbourne.

COURSE CONFIGURATION

Research into previous white water Olympic venues revealed that the Athens course, while dramatic to watch because it had a massive 6.2m head of water, was prohibitively expensive to operate after the Games. Operation of the full course was required even for beginners. Faulkner Browns Architects and the design team of the London course assessed the energy use of various course designs based on their legacy usage profiles and opted for a configuration of two different loops that could be operated independently. Each loop has dedicated pumps sized to match their respective loads, and pump configuration, pipe and valve design were all scrutinised to further improve efficiency.

The 300m-long competition course varies in depth between 2m and 5.5m. Approximately 15 cubic metres of water per second are recirculated through the competition course – roughly equivalent to the amount of water required to fill a 25m swimming pool in 30 seconds. The training course, which is approximately half the length with a maximum drop of 1.6m, uses only 20 per cent of the energy of the Olympic course. This represents significant savings and means that after the Games, the LVRPA will be able to tailor the operation of the two courses to suit the activities at the centre at any given time. The competition course may only be required for special events. Even during the Games, the training course can be used for warm-up events, so that the competition course is only used when necessary.

WATER SUPPLY

Aside from the energy required to pump the water, the other major sustainability issue related to the LVWWC was the water supply itself and how to meet the ODA's target for a 40 per cent reduction in potable water demand. Obvious solutions such as a lake excavated into the groundwater table or connection to the surface waters of the Lee navigation system were ruled out because of poor water quality due to a contaminated site and the potential

81 South-facing terrace with deep roof overhang.

82 Site plan situating facilities building in relation to lake and water courses. The training course uses only 20 per cent of the energy required for the competition course, and they can be operated independently.

83 Bar chart comparing energy consumption of Lee Valley White Water Centre to canoe courses of past Olympic Games and showing low operational energy use of facilities building in relation to the water courses.

84 (Overleaf) View of the Lee Valley White Water Centre entrance. The building is partly embedded in the ground to take advantage of thermal mass and minimise its visual impact in the landscape.

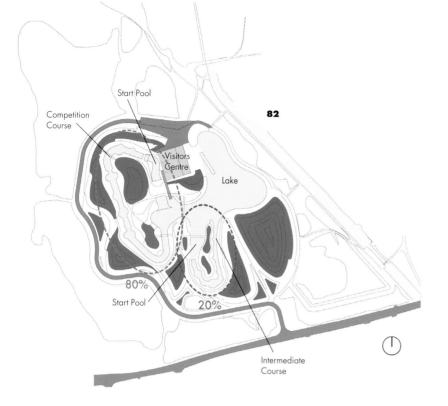

82

Competition
Course

Start Pool

Visitors
Centre

Lake

80%

Start Pool

20%

Intermediate
Course

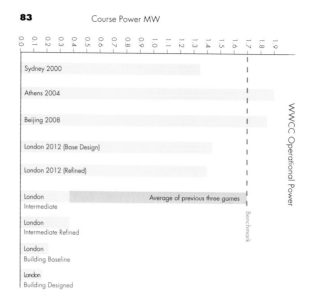

83   Course Power MW

0.0 0.1 0.2 0.3 0.4 0.5 0.6 0.7 0.8 0.9 1.0 1.1 1.2 1.3 1.4 1.5 1.6 1.7 1.8 1.9

Sydney 2000

Athens 2004

Beijing 2008

London 2012 (Base Design)

London 2012 (Refined)

London
Intermediate   Average of previous three games

London
Intermediate Refined

London
Building Baseline

London
Building Designed

WWCC Operational Power

Benchmark

impact on the area's surface water flows. The optimal solution proved to be construction of a new fully lined 10,000m² lake, which is approximately 1.2m deep. The lake must have a sufficient volume of water to supply the course with as small a surface area as possible to minimise evaporation. The lake's water supply is a closed system supplied through a borehole that eliminates the demand for potable water to top up the lake. Measures such as setting the overflow level for the lake high so that any rainfall can be captured ensure that extraction from the aquifer is kept to a minimum.

FACILITIES BUILDING

The facilities building is integrated into the landscape design of the water courses and the lake to maximise views and enable easy access into the starting pools. Split into two levels with distinctively different characters, it includes a reception, café and viewing terrace above, with changing rooms, a boat store and a plant room below.

> *'The building was designed for legacy. We knew it had to be capable of handling the Games, but the real driver was long-term value for Lee Valley [Park Authority] as part of their estate.'*
>
> MICHAEL HALL, FAULKNER BROWNS

The timber-clad – Western Red Cedar – upper level opens to the views and is wrapped with an outdoor terrace while the masonry lower level opens onto the training course. Operable timber louvres open the upper level to the terrace when the pavilion is open but otherwise remain closed for security. Geothermal ground source heat pumps, whose coils are located under the lake, supply heat to the majority of spaces in the building via underfloor heating

and radiators. A rainwater harvesting tank supplies water for toilet flushing, and a solar thermal array with a PV pump provides hot water to the changing rooms.

LANDSCAPE

American landscape practice Michael van Valkenburgh Associates (MVVA) proposed a rolling landscape of earth mounds up to 11m high to create a sense of enclosure around the lake and the courses. LOCOG requirements for temporary seating mean that landscape works can only be completed after the Games. A survey of nearby construction sites and projects in the pipeline has been undertaken to identify local sources of fill for the landscaping works to stockpile material and minimise lorry transport.

In contrast with previous Games, the project team's thorough approach to reducing the energy intensity of the water course combined with the design of an attractive venue

85 Environmental diagram of building illustrating deep overhangs and window reveals to control solar gain.

86 Environmental section of the Lee Valley White Water Centre site illustrating the use of a ground source heat pump and solar thermal panels for the facilities building.

87 Conveyor that takes competitors from the finish lake to the starting point. The finish lake acts as a thermal store for base heating and cooling loads.

88 New 10,000 m² lake supplies water for the canoe courses at the Lee Valley White Water Centre. Water for the 1.2m-deep lake is supplied from a borehole.

85

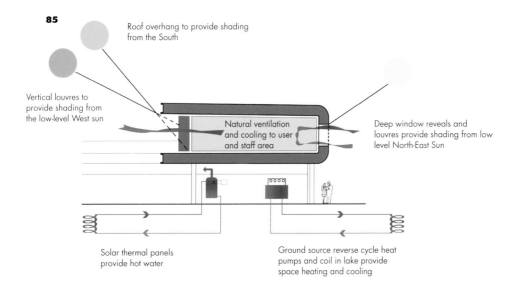

Roof overhang to provide shading from the South

Vertical louvres to provide shading from the low-level West sun

Natural ventilation and cooling to user and staff area

Deep window reveals and louvres provide shading from low level North-East Sun

Solar thermal panels provide hot water

Ground source reverse cycle heat pumps and coil in lake provide space heating and cooling

86

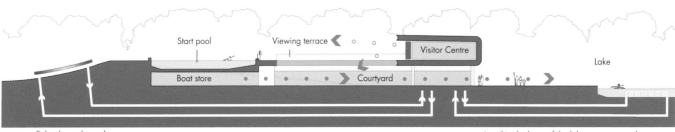

Start pool

Viewing terrace

Visitor Centre

Lake

Boat store

Courtyard

Solar thermal panels supply hot water

A coil in the base of the lake serves ground source heat pump for heating and cooling

appropriately scaled for regional use make the Lee Valley White Water Centre's viability in legacy highly promising. The low curved form of the slim timber building sits comfortably in the valley landscape. Its concrete lower floor dedicated to boat storage, which will be heavily used by wet athletes, is robust and durable. The clever separation of the competition course from the amateur course offers greater operational flexibility going forward for the LVRPA, saving both money and energy. The entire complex was designed with a constant eye on its long-term use.

KEY POINTS

Introduction of a second water course which uses 20% of energy of competition
   course and can be operated independently both during the Games and in legacy
Scrutinising design of competition course to reduce energy demand
Use of borehole to supply lake for watercourse to minimise impact on groundwater
Extensive use of swales and wetland planting to control surface water runoff
Modest facilities building integrated with landscape and designed for legacy use

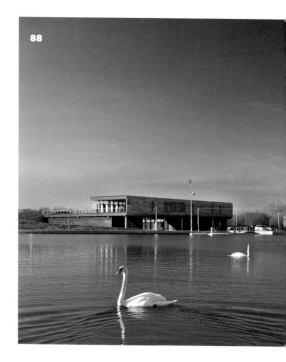

Infrastructure Buildings

The outstanding quality of the infrastructure buildings on the Olympic Park, a major legacy achievement of London 2012, has raised the bar for the design of this building type. The ODA's brief called for utility buildings designed with pride that demonstrate their functionality. Even though the buildings had three different utility clients – EDF, Cofely East London Energy and Thames Water, they were funded in part or in full by the ODA. None of the three utility providers had a track record of working with architects. Without the ODA's vision for a 'family' of high-quality utility buildings, the default solution would have been a series of brick or aluminium-clad boxes with shed roofs.

After the removal of all the electricity pylons from the site and the installation of more than 100km of electric cabling, NORD's substation was the first on site and completed in October 2009. Its sculptural massing and perforated brick detailing informed the design of John McAslan + Partners Energy Centres.

John Lyall Architects won the competition for the Pudding Mill Lane Pumping Station because the strong architectural form of their proposed circular building, based on the shape of the station's underground shaft, appealed to the ODA, which was fully funding this project. Thames Water signed off on the project as the building's end operator, but the design

'These buildings developed incrementally, each informing
the other throughout the design process. There was a lot
of conversation between the designers, which was quite
pleasing to see from the client's point of view. This shows
what you can do with a utility building if you apply
a little imagination. These could have been the worst
buildings in the Park.'

KEVIN OWENS, DESIGN PRINCIPAL, LOCOG

89 View looking north towards 'family' of infrastructure buildings on the west side of the Olympic Park (from left to right): Olympic Energy Centre, Primary Substation, with Handball Arena beyond.

was developed jointly with the ODA. Delighted with the final building, Thames Water
then commissioned Lyall directly for three more projects in the Olympic Park precinct and
subsequently for Crossness Sewage Treatment Works, a new plant further east along the
Thames, due to complete in 2012. This is a direct outcome of the Olympic Park work.

All the infrastructure buildings have been sized to suit the Park's legacy development, with the
exception of the Old Ford Water Recycling Plant which is a pilot project. Citing the durability
of engineer Joseph Bazalgette's Victorian buildings, Lyall opted for robust materials that were
built to last for well over 100 years as permanent infrastructure. This emphasis on durability
and long life is a critical aspect of sustainable design that is often overlooked and frequently
undermined by material and product warranties of much shorter duration.

Primary Substation

Its robust brick construction, a reference to Stratford's heritage of nineteenth-century industrial buildings, is built to last and the building is flexible to accommodate changing plant in the future. The building form responds to the urban context and the subtlety of its brick detailing enlivens the façade and gives it an urban presence both from afar and for nearby pedestrians.

Robustness, flexibility and lean structural engineering inform the design of the Substation. As the first building to be completed on the Olympic Park, its architectural quality set a high standard for the remainder of London 2012's infrastructure projects. The ODA's brief called for a building with a sense of permanence that simultaneously paid heed to aesthetics and sustainability, including whole life cycle costs. The Substation powered construction work on the Olympic Park site and is sized to supply the Park and Stratford City during the Games and in legacy.

> 'The building design is all about legacy; our chief concern was the longest possible asset life in terms of renewal and refitting.'
>
> LIAM G. O'SULLIVAN, UK POWER NETWORKS (CLIENT)

Abutting the railway line by the west entrance to the Park near Hackney Wick, the Substation, along with the Energy Centre, forms a pair of utility buildings that will serve future generations of east Londoners. It houses three transformers and a switch room that convert electricity from the London Power Network and link to more than 100km of underground electric cables in the Park and Stratford City. Nearby power stations at Bow and Hackney have a capacity of 48MVA and 90MVA respectively, so the new Substation, with its capacity of 198MVA, more than doubles electricity supply to this part of east London.

The massing of the 70m-long building is modulated by locating the higher volumes that house the transformers and cooling towers as bookends to the lower switch room in the middle. Inside the Substation, a 132,000 volt input is stepped down to three 11,000V outputs through three 110-tonne transformers. Sourced from Australia for their energy-efficient design, the transformers were shipped to the UK by boat. Security was a major aspect of the design, and NORD Architecture early on proposed that the sculptural exterior wall of the building define the security line to eliminate fencing. Where required, a welded wire fence with a dark powder coated finish was used to minimise its visual impact. Views from above onto the roof from the new land bridge east of the site were carefully considered. The open cooling towers are enclosed with a mesh that provides a visual screen for the plant

ENVIRONMENTAL PROFILE

Capacity: 198 MVA

Function: To step down electricity from the London Power Network from 132kV to 11kV

Annual CO_2 emissions: 2.31 kg/m_2 (occupied); 1.68kg/m^2 (unoccupied)

MATERIALS

Primary materials: brick, concrete

Materials with recycled content: in situ concrete, blockwork

Reclaimed materials: crushed brick and gravel on biodiverse roof

Innovative approach: EDF's first use of architects to design a substation that relates to its urban context and serves as a memorable urban landmark

90 The robust angular massing of the Primary Substation holds its own within the Lea Valley's post-industrial landscape.

equipment below. To promote biodiversity, the lower portion of the roof has a brown roof system made of crushed brick and gravel reclaimed from the site.

The building's defining visual quality is the detailing of the brick, which uses three different bonds to create variety and shadowplay on the façade. Use of bricks reclaimed from the Olympic Park site – of which there were 150 tonnes – was initially considered, but load testing determined that they were not strong enough to resist the required structural and design blast loadings and 4-hour fire rating. A clay engineering brick by Ibstock was eventually specified. Perforations in the upper portion of the wall, created by omitting headers in two out of three brick courses, provide ventilation for the cooling towers. Dramatic when backlit, the Substation is a strong orienting landmark at night.

Lighting was selected based on suitability for task, luminaire efficiency and lamp life. The majority of fittings are high-efficiency fluorescents, though in areas where instant response bright light is required for security purposes, LEDs were used in place of conventional halogens. EDF is trialling a new BEMS at the Substation to closely monitor the building services.

Recognised with a Royal Institute of British Architects (RIBA) award in 2010, the Substation successfully marries an honest expression of the building's structure and function with an inventive use of brick to create a memorable building. Its robustness also enhances its durability and its likelihood of a long life, an aspect of sustainable design that is often skimmed over. It will sit comfortably in the urban landscape as nearby development sites fill in and serve as an orienting landmark for both area residents and visitors to the Park. It exudes quality, durability and efficiency, important values to associate both with energy provision and with London 2012's legacy.

91 Aerial view. The rectangular forms of the Primary Substation are at the top with the Olympic Energy Centre beyond and the Handball Arena to the right.

92 Projecting headers add visual interest by creating a play of shadows on the attractive brick façade.

93 Exploded diagram showing how the Primary Substation's massing and the use of different brick bonding mitigates its monolithic form.

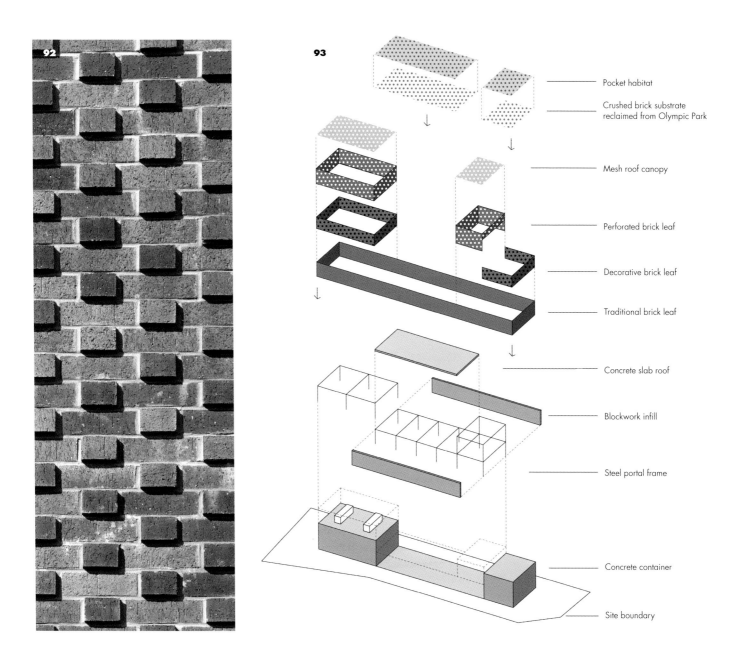

92

93

Pocket habitat

Crushed brick substrate
reclaimed from Olympic Park

Mesh roof canopy

Perforated brick leaf

Decorative brick leaf

Traditional brick leaf

Concrete slab roof

Blockwork infill

Steel portal frame

Concrete container

Site boundary

KEY POINTS

Building massing relates to surrounding context to integrate in future urban development
   and mitigate bulk of building for pedestrians

Brick used for robustness and durability

Exquisite brick detailing enlivens what would otherwise be a monolithic façade

Internal volume flexible should equipment configuration change

Olympic Park Energy Centre and Stratford Energy Centre

District-wide energy provision to the Olympic Park site, both during the Games and post-Games, is London 2012's single most important environmental achievement along with the Olympic Park itself. Although most of the infrastructure is underground, two new energy buildings house the plant that powers the new development. The buildings are easily identifiable landmarks in the new urban fabric of east London and serve as explicit reminders of where and how energy is generated.

Construction of inner-city power buildings was a first for GDF Suez Energy Services, who will operate the Olympic Park Energy Centres through its subsidiary Cofely East London Energy on a 40-year concession arrangement. The lightweight modular design of the Energy Centres reflects an evolution in energy-generation technology and contrasts markedly with the heavy masonry construction of Bankside (now Tate Modern) and Battersea Power Stations designed by Giles Gilbert Scott. Likewise, their community setting adjacent to the Olympic Park differs from the prominent Thames-side sites of the earlier buildings. At the west entrance to the Park, the Olympic Park Energy Centre at Kings Yard primarily supplies the Park venues and future development sites to the west. A second slightly smaller plant outside the eastern park boundary serves Stratford City and the Westfield retail complex. The energy centres provide heating, cooling and electricity via a gas-fired CCHP and a biomass plant at Kings Yard (see p. 68 for more on district heating).

A public path that links to Hackney Wick stations passes within 9m of the main Energy Centre. Although it is located back of house during the Games, it will eventually sit alongside the Substation (see p. 160) in a community context when nearby sites are developed. To mitigate the monolithic façade of the 18m-high building, the architects introduced glazing so that passersby can see inside. The whole is cloaked in a Cor-ten steel mesh that creates a subtle play of light on the façade with changing weather. The only external expression of the building's function is an enormous flue and two 20m-high

ENERGY OUTPUT THROUGH THE GAMES

Olympic Park Energy Centre: 121MW heating, 25MW cooling, 16.5MW power

Stratford Energy Centre: 75MW heating, 39MW cooling, 13.5MW power

EXISTING PLANT WITH POTENTIAL FOR EXPANSION IN LEGACY

Olympic Park Energy Centre: one 3.3MW CCHP engine, with room for four more

One 3MW biomass boiler in nearby Edwardian building, with room for one more

Two 20MW dual fuel boilers supplement CCHP to meet peak heating demands

Stratford Energy Centre: two 3.3MW CCHP engines with room for two more

MATERIALS

Primary materials: concrete, steel, timber

Materials with recycled content: recycled aggregate in concrete piles, pile caps and in situ topping to floors, Structural Insulated Panels (SIPS) with recyclable insulation in middle layer, blockwork

Reclaimed materials: crushed material from Olympic Park site used for piling mat

Innovative approach and products: location of major power stations in community setting, SIPs with factory-bonded EPDM

94 The Olympic Park Energy Centre is designed to be a community landmark in the tradition of Bankside (now Tate Modern) and Battersea Power Stations. Today's technologies mean that lighter-weight steel construction replaces heavy masonry. A 45m-high flue is clad in Cor-ten steel mesh.

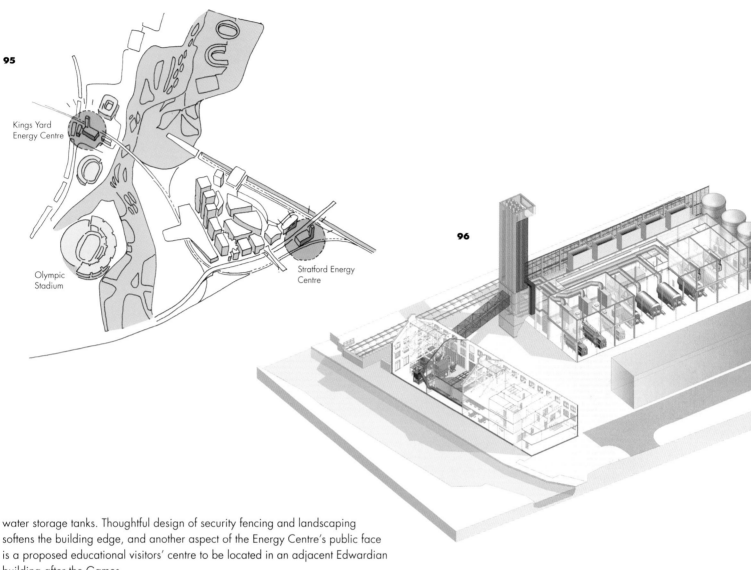

95

Kings Yard
Energy Centre

Olympic
Stadium

Stratford Energy
Centre

96

water storage tanks. Thoughtful design of security fencing and landscaping softens the building edge, and another aspect of the Energy Centre's public face is a proposed educational visitors' centre to be located in an adjacent Edwardian building after the Games.

DESIGN DEVELOPMENT

The architects' brief was for a robust building with a modular façade where panels could be removed in the event of plant breakdown or replacement. A flexible arrangement of louvres to ventilate the plant equipment was also required because equipment locations had not yet been determined and equipment could change in the future. Resisting Cofely's standard aluminium panel solution, John McAslan + Partners took its cue from the Substation's perforated brick screen, opting for a durable, self-finishing cladding of Cor-ten steel mesh. The screen acts as a veil over a steel structure with a façade of Structural Insulated Panels (SIP) factory-bonded with an EPDM (ethylene propylene diene Monomer) synthetic rubber layer for waterproofing. Where ventilation is required, louvres are inserted within a strip in the panelled façade behind the continuous Cor-ten veil, a flexible system that can be adapted if the kit inside the building changes. It is all demountable when maintenance is required.

95 Sketch site plan of Olympic Park showing location of two energy centres. The Olympic Park Energy Centre at the western boundary of the Park serves the Olympic Park venues and future development sites to the west. A second energy centre on the Stratford side of the Park serves Stratford City, Westfield and future development to the east.

96 Axonometric showing relationship between Olympic Park Energy Centre and existing Edwardian building that houses biomass boilers. Both buildings have spare capacity to house additional equipment as energy demand increases when further sites are developed in legacy.

97 After the Games, a pedestrian path linking the Olympic Park to Hackney Wick station will pass within 19m of the Olympic Park Energy Centre. Glazing at the base of the building provides interesting views inside for passers-by.

As with other venues, CLM required the design team to fill out a Waste Minimisation Action Report, a spreadsheet that lists all the project's materials and identifies opportunities for reuse of materials from the Olympic Park site, waste reduction by dimensioning to minimise offcuts, and possibilities for recycling of materials. The SIP manufacturer was selected because the insulation layer between the OSB boards could be ground down and recycled. Cor-ten can also be recycled. EPDM rolls were manufactured to the required dimensions to minimise offcuts. Throughout the design process, liaison with the ODA team ensured that any stockpiled materials available on the site were incorporated where possible. Hardcore and fill from the Olympic Park were used to lay the mat for the pile rig; topsoil was also supplied from the Park. Although a hard surface that can take service vehicles was required in the forecourt, the designers pushed for a random paving layout that allows vegetation to grow between the pavers.

FLEXIBILITY
The 65m-long by 29m-wide building is sized to accommodate future expansion, and for the Games the building volume is only partially occupied. Because plant equipment was procured simultaneously with the building design, the brief was for a flexible space that could accommodate a wide range of installations and changing technology in the future.

'The ODA made you focus on the building's future and material choices ... At one of the first reviews, we were asked about the future use of this building at the end of the 40-year life cycle. That kind of thinking right at the beginning was different. The ODA was always there to help and contribute ideas.'

AARON PEXTON, ASSOCIATE, JOHN MCASLAN + PARTNERS

Legacy uses for the post-40-year contract period were also considered. Because the steel and precast concrete structure can accommodate heavy loads, it could easily be adapted to a four-storey office building by inserting a mezzanine level. Conversion to an art museum or other cultural institution similar to Tate Modern would also be possible.

The creation of community-based energy buildings partially fuelled by local renewable resources is a logical way forward because it saves energy and reduces transmission losses from remote power plants. The challenge is how to modulate the massive scale of these buildings in a neighbourhood setting. The shoebox forms of the Olympic Park site's two Cor-ten hangars sit comfortably in Stratford's post-industrial landscape. The crisp steel mesh whose front surface self-finishes by corrosion is likely to age well, and the perforated screen catches the light in different ways, providing visual variety across the enormous façade. As they evolve over time into local landmarks, they will also promote a more direct relationship between energy providers and consumers, a welcome development in these energy-conscious times.

KEY POINTS
Energy building as an outward-facing community landmark integrated in urban fabric
Flexible design for changing technology and for long-term change of use
Modular design with flexible louvre zone for breathing façade
Designing in extra capacity for future expansion

98 Elevation study showing the relationship of the Olympic Park Energy Centre and the Primary Substation to the existing urban context. A primary design consideration was that these buildings should serve as community landmarks after the Games.

99 The Olympic Park Energy Centre was designed as the mechanical plant was being specified so it had to be flexible at the outset but also in legacy as technologies change.

98

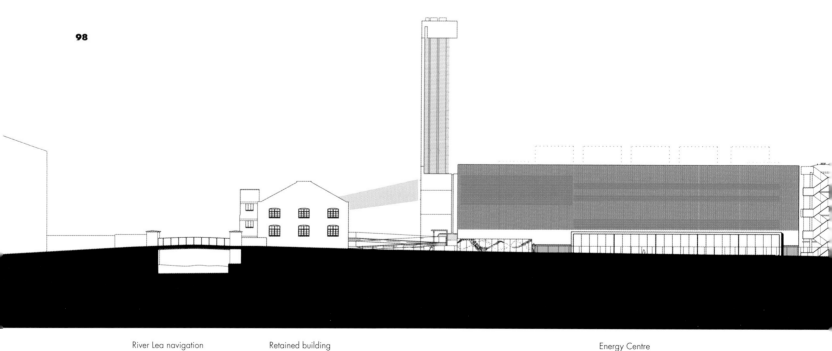

River Lea navigation   Retained building   Energy Centre

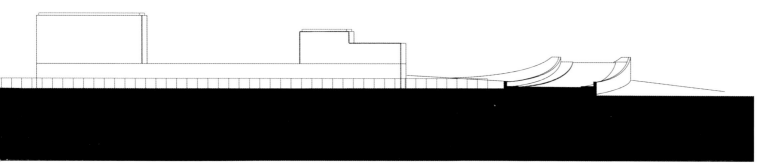

Primary Substation

Waterden Road

Pudding Mill Lane Pumping Station

This project is the result of sheer ingenuity. It displays an inventiveness and resourcefulness that thinks outside the box – literally. The architects challenged the civil engineers to disassemble the equipment required for the pumping station into its component parts and then fashioned an efficient building that makes those parts explicit. Design elements such as an illuminated flue tower, bright pink odour filtration tanks and the printing of nineteenth-century engineering drawings on the exterior walls transform what could have been an unsightly utilitarian shed into a memorable building full of visual delight.

At 325 square metres, the Pudding Mill Lane Pumping Station might be one of the smallest structures built in the Olympic Park, yet symbolically it is one of the most significant. It is the only above-ground evidence of the new 1.8km long sewer network that lies below the Park. The Pumping Station collects all the sewage from the new gravity-fed sewers under the Park – sized for both the Games and for future development afterwards – and pumps it 21m up to meet the Northern Outfall Sewer (NOS) which runs under the Greenway (see p. 16) along the south-west boundary of the Olympic Park site. From there, sewage makes its way to Beckton Sewage Treatment Works, where solid matter is removed as sludge and the effluent is cleaned and discharged into the Thames.

The ODA brief called for a building that expressed this function and enhanced the public realm by providing an orienting landmark and visual interest for pedestrians. It is clearly visible from the nearby DLR platform, from the Greenway cycle path and from passing trains.

John Lyall Architects challenged Thames Water's approved outline design for a brick shed and worked with the civil engineers to understand the station's component parts. 'Our design was very economic. When we started, a huge square shed was going to be built over the circular underground shaft; it would have required its own foundation. We discovered that to keep the circular caisson down in the ground with the ground water trying to push it up, a massive concrete collar – 4ft deep by 1.5ft wide – was required. So we proposed using the collar as a foundation for the Pumping Station. That saved a lot of money, a lot of energy, a lot of concrete and a lot of time.'

ENVIRONMENTAL PROFILE

CEEQUAL: Excellent 93.8%

Recycled content (proportion of secondary materials as percentage of value): 11% (target 8%)

Recycled aggregate (proportion of secondary materials as percentage of mass): 76%

MATERIALS

Main materials: precast concrete, steel

Materials with recycled content: in situ concrete

Innovative materials, products, technologies or approaches: expressing engineering components in architectural form; bird and bat boxes cast into precast sections

100 The illuminated 'flue' of the Pudding Mill Lane Pumping Station evacuates odours from the pink odour filtration tanks and doubles as a beacon by night.

'Our design was very economic … we proposed using the collar as a foundation for the Pumping Station. That saved a lot of money, a lot of energy, a lot of concrete and a lot of time.'

JOHN LYALL, ARCHITECT

101 Pudding Mill Lane Pumping Station is an engaging building that expresses the function of its different parts replaces what otherwise would have been a nondescript brick shed.

This leanness of design is the building's most important environmental achievement, but equally important is its role in enhancing the public realm. Odour filtration tanks painted bright pink – lifted from the London 2012 colour palette – make the building instantly recognisable by day, and by night a 12m-high illuminated lantern on the plant's ventilation shaft provides an orienting landmark on the route to the nearby DLR station. Other aspects of the design enrich the building at close range: engineering drawings of Bazalgette's nearby Victorian pumping station are etched on the building's precast concrete exterior, and the precast panels are pigmented to two different shades to add further visual interest. Particular attention has been paid to select an attractive perforated mesh fencing material for the site perimeter and to create openings in the boundary wall to allow views in. One can easily imagine the Pumping Station sitting comfortably in the mixed-use development envisaged for the south side of the Park in future.

Construction materials were selected for robustness as well as visual appearance. The choice of precast rather than in situ concrete for the Pumping Station shaft and walls minimised material waste. The Pumping Station's modular array of pumps is designed to operate efficiently to meet requirements during the Games; in the early post-Games period, fewer pumps will be needed to meet demand, and then as the area develops, additional pumps

102 Building section of Pudding Mill Lane Pumping Station. The building's round form reflects the circular underground shaft of the dry well.

103 Diagram explaining the operation of the Pudding Mill Lane Pumping Station.

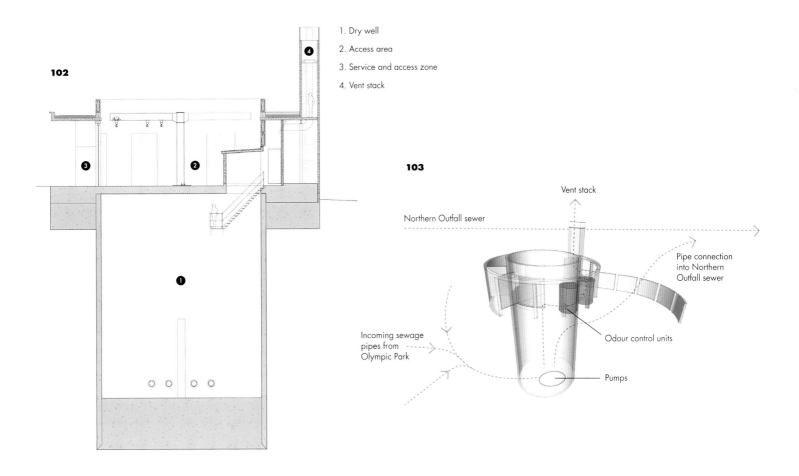

102

1. Dry well
2. Access area
3. Service and access zone
4. Vent stack

103

Vent stack

Northern Outfall sewer

Pipe connection into Northern Outfall sewer

Incoming sewage pipes from Olympic Park

Odour control units

Pumps

104 Early etching of the Pumping Station depicting it as a new landmark in east London's industrial landscape.

105 Detail of Joseph Bazalgette's drawings for Victorian sewerworks embossed on precast concrete panels on the Pudding Mill Lane Pumping Station.

106 Signage on the Greenway. The Pumping Station is visible from the nearby Greenway and the adjacent DLR station. Its recognisable form will make it a landmark in this rapidly changing urban quarter.

107 Exploded axonometric of Pudding Mill Lane Pumping Station building elements, explaining functions of the pumping station.

106

can be brought into service so that the plant always operates at maximum efficiency.

To address biodiversity, the building's doughnut-shaped brown roof is planted with sedum, and 13 bird and bat boxes have been incorporated into the eaves of the precast concrete shaft. 'So detailed were the ODA's requirements that all plant species had to be specified to be indigenous to the UK, leading to a specialist seed mix for the green roof, and the selection of a field maple tree and other local bushes for the compound. The bird and bat boxes also had to be oriented in particular directions, and adequately spaced to avoid inter-species rivalry! Working to such high standards was a great experience, and continues to inform our ongoing work,' John Lyall, Architect.

The Pudding Mill Lane Pumping Station's enduring quality stems from its visual delight. An architecture that expresses its function and the engineering drawings embossed in the concrete invite passersby to engage with the building and understand its purpose. Its circular forms and its dash of pink paint combine to create a memorable building that serves as an orienting landmark in an area currently devoid of reference points.

KEY POINTS
Sets a precedent for high quality design of utility building
Bespoke design tailored to engineering components rather than rectangular shed
Enhances public realm
Increases public awareness of sewage treatment
Sewers sized for legacy
Green roof and bird and bat boxes enhance biodiversity

107

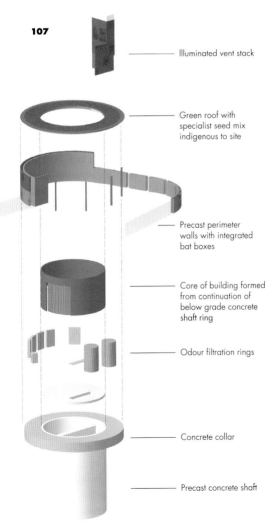

Illuminated vent stack

Green roof with specialist seed mix indigenous to site

Precast perimeter walls with integrated bat boxes

Core of building formed from continuation of below grade concrete shaft ring

Odour filtration rings

Concrete collar

Precast concrete shaft

Old Ford Water Recycling Plant

Jointly funded by the ODA and Thames Water as a pilot research project, the Old Ford Water Recycling Plant is one of London 2012's flagship sustainability initiatives, due to the innovative nature of the water cleansing technology.

The Old Ford Water Treatment Plant takes sewage from the Northern Outfall Sewer and cleans it through a multi-step process before recirculating it to irrigate the Olympic Park. Wet sewage passes through two enormous sediment tanks sited outside the building where large refuse such as timber and rags are removed and a chemical process starts to break down the remaining sludge. The effluent then passes into tanks inside the building where 3m-long strips of plastic remove the majority of micro-organisms. The 12m height of the building is determined by the clearance required above the tanks to change and wash these membranes, which are removed vertically. Another chemical process further cleans the water, which then passes into a holding tank from which it is distributed into a network that irrigates the Olympic Park and supplies water for toilet flushing in all legacy venues except the Aquatics Centre which has its own non-potable supply from filter backwash.

Located in a small area of woodland immediately south of the Olympic Stadium, the building is designed to disappear into the landscape. Developed with the input of the London Wildlife Trust, habitat features and a new pond have been designed to enhance biodiversity on the site. The ODA was keen for the building design to reflect the innovative nature of the technology it houses. Early scheme designs explored a glulam structure with rammed earth walls.

'We were given licence by the ODA to think freely and they supported us. They wanted everyone in the team to think outside the box. Whereas if we were working with a utility company, it might have been a bit of a battle to make them think innovatively.'

JOHN LYALL, ARCHITECT

In the end, Thames Water and the ODA agreed upon a larch-clad steel structure. Gabion walls, which can be colonised by birds and insects, enhance biodiversity and provide a robust finish to the base of the building. Interestingly, the final planning decision made was to use crushed Somerset stone, as it was felt that it blended in better with the surroundings, despite the ODA's view that material from the Olympic Park site should be reused. Cor-ten

ENVIRONMENTAL PROFILE

Water recycling capacity for legacy: 0.5Ml/day

MATERIALS

Main materials: Somerset stone, larch

Materials with recycled content: N/A

Innovative materials, products, technologies or approaches: water recycling technology at this scale is a UK first; Kingspan SIPs clad with larch, biodiverse green roof with 'London mix'

108 Visualisation of Old Ford Water Recycling Plant. One of the key sustainability initiatives of London 2012, this facility cleanses water from the Northern Outfall Sewer for toilet flushing in the Olympic Stadium and all legacy venues and irrigation of the Park, reducing overall drinking water demand by approximately 40 per cent.

Towpath

Note 1

Note 5

PUMP STATION
+5.00 approx.

RELOCATED BALLAST MATERIAL

Note 4

Butterfly
mound

Note 1

ecoblock

Note 5

Note 5

Note 5

WATER RECYCLING
FACILITY

Note 5

Access track

+5.00 approx.

Note 2

ow level bridge

Note 1

Note 1

th level bridge

+9.50

Notes 1+3

sliding doors complete the scheme. The treatment plant, which is overlooked by nearby apartment blocks, has an extensive biodiverse green roof, planted with a purposely developed 'London mix', and Grasscrete pavers provide the hard surface required for service vehicles. Determined to add a splash of colour similar to the Pudding Mill Pumping Station, the architects proposed painting the sediment tanks turquoise, but given the natural setting, the final colour is a discrete green that will be visible in the spaces between the larch cladding boards.

The Old Ford Water Recycling Plant illustrates well how the momentum of the Olympic Games facilitates innovation. The Park-wide target for reduction of potable water use created an incentive for the ODA to consider a broad range of solutions. A design partnership with Thames Water, already trialled at Pudding Mill Lane, enabled this innovative water recycling technology to be piloted for the Olympic Park.

109 The landscape plan for the Old Ford Water Recycling Plant site introduced new planting to enhance biodiversity and cleared invasive species.

110 Gabion walls and larch cladding were specified to be in keeping with the woodland setting. View looking south with the Old Ford Pumping Station on the left.

111 Visualisation of Old Ford Water Recycling Plant.

KEY POINTS
Innovative water recycling technology
Self-finishing low maintenance materials
Integration with woodland setting

110

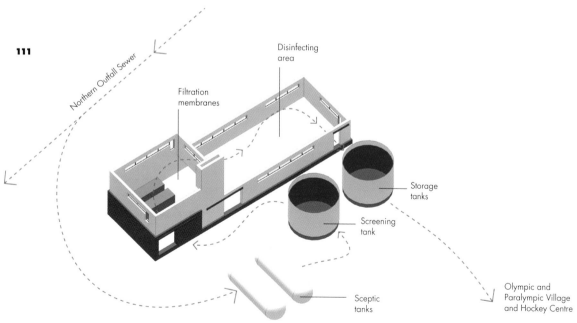

111

Northern Outfall Sewer

Filtration
membranes

Disinfecting
area

Storage
tanks

Screening
tank

Sceptic
tanks

Olympic and
Paralympic Village
and Hockey Centre

Old Ford Ground Water Pumping Station

Thames Water has reactivated a disused well in a nature reserve just south of the Olympic Stadium. The scheme dissembles the pump's components into five steel-cubes that are randomly sited among the trees in a woodland setting.

The Olympic Park site required more drinking water and this modest project makes use of an existing Victorian well in a small nature reserve south of the Stadium. Water from the 60m-deep well is pumped to the Lea Valley reservoir. As with the sewer pumping station, John Lyall Architects interrogated the components of the brief and designed a scheme sympathetic to the woodland setting. Four cubes clad in Cor-ten steel (selected because it is robust and self-finishing) house a control room, a sample room, a transformer room and a conservation room for the Wildlife Trust, which maintains the site. A larger fifth cube is the centrepiece, housing the well head and pumps and is clad in perforated Cor-ten mesh with digital patterns derived from winter photographs of trees on the site. As with the Pudding Mill Lane Pumping Station, the architects' inventiveness and flair led them to a clever solution that addresses the technical challenges of the project with an inspirational solution well suited to its natural setting.

MATERIALS

Main materials: Cor-ten

Materials with recycled content: N/A

Innovative approach: dividing programme into several small cubes to reduce impact on woodland setting

KEY POINTS
Integration with woodland setting
Self-finishing low-maintenance materials

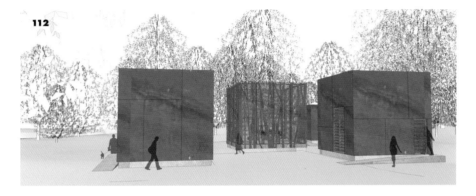

112

112 Visualisation of the cubes in the woodland setting. Division of the Old Ford Ground Water Pumping Station into smaller parts reduces its overall scale so that it becomes like a sculpture.

113 Axonometric showing five Corten-clad cubes. The larger central cube houses the pumping equipment that supplies potable water to the Olympic Park.

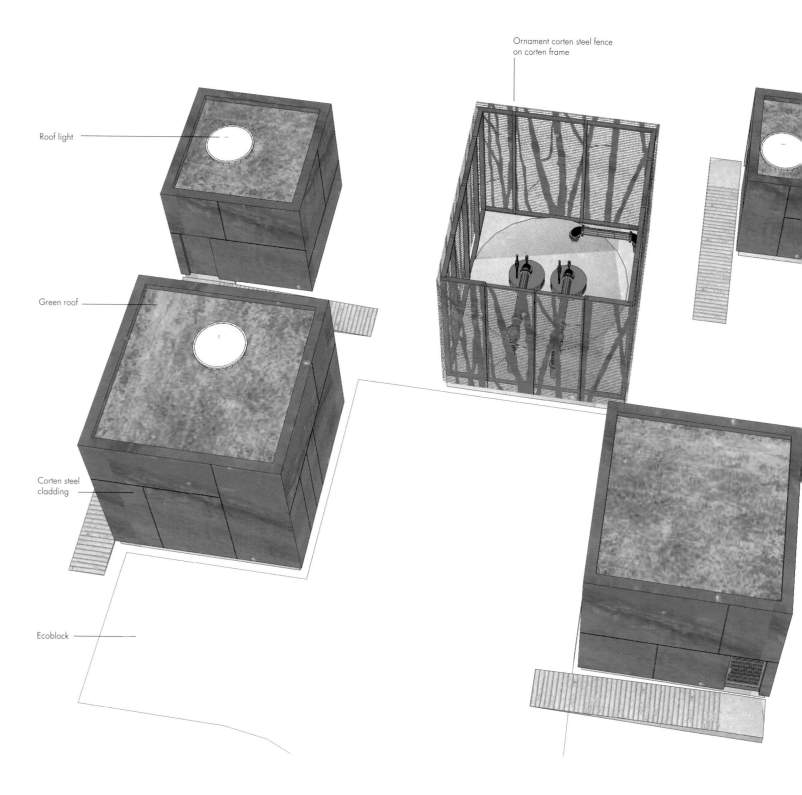

Roof light

Green roof

Corten steel
cladding

Ecoblock

Ornament corten steel fence
on corten frame

Stratford Box

The Stratford Box is a pumping station that relieves potential groundwater build-up near Stratford rail station in the event of a change in the water table that could cause flooding on the Eurostar line. A random geometry of interlocking slabs transforms this ground water pumping station into a sculptural outcropping of horizontal slabs and planting.

In the Stratford Box, a series of stepped boxes made of oversized clay blocks house a substation, a control room and a water recycling unit. Some are topped with hard surfaces for access; others have green roofs and planters. Two types of bird boxes are built into the walls. A nearby balancing pond serves the dual purpose of absorbing excess water and providing a biodiverse habitat for wildlife. The site is not accessible to the public, but is visible from nearby bridges and passing trains. As with the Old Ford, what could have been a utilitarian engineered solution has been configured by John Lyall Architects into an inspired mosaic of paving and planting, clearly visible from nearby bridges and railway lines.

MATERIALS

Main materials: clay block

Materials with recycled content: N/A

Innovative approaches: integration of pumping station components into the landscape with stepped form and planted roofs

KEY POINTS
Pumping station integrated into landscape as visually attractive feature
Biodiversity provided through balancing pond and bird boxes

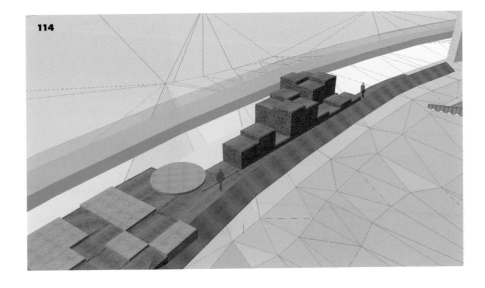

114

114 Green roofs and planting integrate the Stratford Box with the landscape.

115 Located east of the Olympic Park near Stratford Station, the Stratford Box discharges excess ground water that could flood the Eurostar line. The interlocking rectangular forms that enclose plant equipment appear as a sculpture in the landscape from nearby bridges and passing trains.

Other Park Buildings

Accommodation for the media is an important feature of every Olympic and Paralympic Games. A press building and a broadcast building are located in the northwest corner of the Olympic Park. Due to the large amount of space required, they represent one of the biggest challenges for legacy use.

116 IBC/MPC Complex, Multi-Storey car park. The majority of press and broadcasters will arrive at the Olympic site by bus or car during the Games. A bridge link at first floor level provides access over the Loop Road to the complex. The bridge makes extensive use of FSC-certified timber: unfinished larch for the wall screens and stressed-skin plywood panels for the roof.

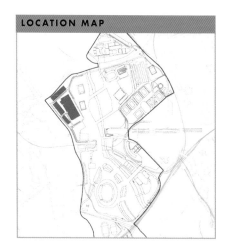

LOCATION MAP

IBC/MPC Complex

The IBC/MPC Complex consists of two buildings: the International Broadcast Centre (IBC) and the Main Press Centre (MPC), designed by RPS, Allies & Morrison (envelope design) and Allies & Morrison respectively. The mismatch between the large amount of floor space required for the media for the Games and the immediate market demand for this type of space in Hackney Wick on the north-western perimeter of the Park has made this project one of the most difficult to deliver of all the London 2012 venues.

The original scheme sought to future-proof the complex by working to set dimensions that would provide flexibility and variety for both commercial and residential uses after the Games; elements of this approach were retained in the project as built.

For the IBC/MPC Complex, as for the Olympic and Paralympic Village, the ODA initially sought a private developer to build the project for the Games and then adapt it for legacy. The International Broadcast Centre – the largest building in the Olympic Park – and the Main Press Centre will serve as a 24-hour media hub for 20,000 broadcasters, journalists and photographers during the Olympic and Paralympic Games. This complex of facilities poses a difficult legacy challenge because approximately 90,000m² of commercial and office space will be on offer immediately after the Games.

Located in the north-west corner of the Park, abutting the A12 and the River Lee Navigation Canal, the buildings are less than a 10-minute walk from Hackney Wick station. A longer 15-minute walk to Stratford's transport hub make this location on the Park a harder sell; nearby Hackney Wick connects only to the London Overground service. During the Games, a car park for over 1,200 cars will serve the complex because many journalists and broadcasters will travel by car to other sporting venues. Due to the planners' objective of reducing car dependency after the Games, half of the car park has temporary planning permission and the building is designed so that half of it can be dismantled. A separate building will provide catering and a 200m-long temporary high street will include banks, shops and a post office.

The IBC/MPC Complex design has undergone various permutations driven by changes in the outlook for its future use due to fluctuation in the property market since the original competition scheme selected in 2007. The thrust of all the proposals has been to create a mix of temporary and permanent buildings that could be subdivided into modules for different sized tenancies in future. The car park has been designed to be downsized with a joint between the permanent

ENVIRONMENTAL PROFILE (FOR BOTH BUILDINGS COMBINED)

BREEAM: Excellent (MPC only)

Predicted CO₂ emissions reduction beyond Part L 2006: 17.5% (MPC only)

Reduction in potable water consumption: 73% (MPC only) – (forecast)

Recycled content (proportion of secondary materials as percentage of value): 22%–25% (22% MSCP, 22.3% MPC and 25.4% IBC).

Recycled aggregate (Proportion of secondary materials as percentage of mass): 33% (includes MSCP, IBC and MPC combined)

Sustainable transport (delivery of materials by rail/water): 59% (forecast)

U-values: N/A

MATERIALS

Main materials: concrete, steel

Materials with recycled content: concrete, carpet

Innovative approaches: testing Games design against legacy scenarios to establish flexible column spacing and floor to floor heights

117 The extensive mechanical plant required to service the media studios at the International Broadcast Centre is located on external gantries and will be removed after the Games.

117

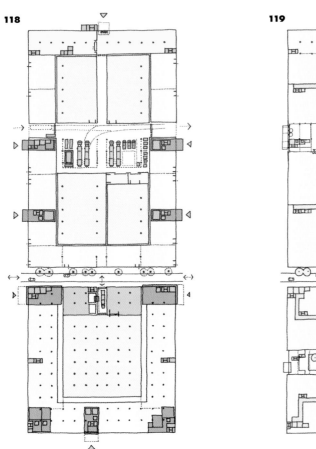
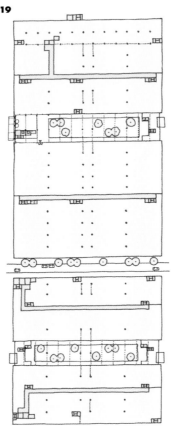

and temporary sections so that part of the building could be removed with minimal impact on the permanent structure.

The constraints of cost and programme have meant that initial aspirations for a mixed use development, which would mitigate the scale of these large buildings by providing residential uses along the canal and a permeable link between the Olympic Park and Hackney Wick to the west, have been difficult to achieve.

IGLOO'S NEON
Neon, the initial scheme designed by Allies & Morrison for the Carillion/Igloo team, envisioned this neighbourhood as Soho East: state of the art studios for the digital media sector with live/work studios and proximity to the Olympic Park. The canal edge was to be exploited for housing, and four architectural practices explored different mews-type housing schemes for the site. Key to the scheme was a mix of uses: living and working, shops, cafés, and restaurants.

With future-proofing in mind, the IBC was initially designed as largely temporary, with

foundations and structure able to be adapted for post-Games occupation by the creative media industry. Potential uses might be studios, sound stages, workshops, galleries, creative manufacturing spaces and offices. As Paul Summerlin of Allies & Morrison observes, 'The IBC in the original proposal was temporary: a fabric container with the structure designed to work with legacy which was being developed in parallel. This was really interesting. We were developing a scheme for the Games and testing the implications for legacy. Legacy impacted on the Games design.'

The building was designed in eight modular blocks on a 9m x 13.5m grid that could accommodate cross-ventilated courtyard schemes with an anticipated occupancy of 10m^2 per person. To be developed in six phases, a variety of lettable space was envisioned with large anchor tenants, medium units for maturing businesses and more affordable smaller spaces for start-ups.

Services were located in east–west corridors between the modules, which were designed to accommodate future streets, with provision allowed for tree planting and street lights. A 'soft zone' in the external cladding of the broadcasting studios allowed for retrofitting windows. Structural connections were demountable and steel components reusable.

During Stage C, BioRegional contributed to Neon's environmental report, which included a useful sustainability matrix, summarising the various requirements of the ODA, planning, BREEAM, Igloo's own 'Footprint' document and BioRegional's One Planet Living principles. Each item in the matrix was classified into one of three clearly distinct categories: must do, should do or aspiration.

118 International Broadcast Centre reuse study: option for creative workspace units arranged between a series of indoor and outdoor access spaces.

119 International Broadcast Centre reuse study: option for recording studios with ancillary/ creative workspace units.

120 View across the north Park to the International Broadcast Centre with gantries of mechanical plant on the exterior. The building is almost twice the length of Tate Modern.

FUTURE-PROOFING

As with the Basketball Arena, a future-proofed building that would be flexible enough to accommodate changing uses and have a basebuild quality adequate to attract the investors and occupiers proposed for Neon required additional investment up front that exceeded the ODA's budgetary and programme constraints. The slowdown in the property market further impacted the viability of the scheme. In September 2008, Igloo Regeneration withdrew and the project was taken forward solely by Carillion with the Games requirements as the primary driver. Nevertheless, the seed notions about the flexibility of the space for legacy use, the importance of the public realm, the importance of east–west permeability and the connection to Hackney Wick are still present in the final scheme.

'The approach to these buildings was forward-thinking when we began [in 2007]. The whole process has moved people's thinking along and has planted seeds about what is a good way to do things. Success cannot be measured only in terms of the Games development.'

PAUL SUMMERLIN, ALLIES & MORRISON

Rather than designing specifically for legacy and then overlaying the Games as in the original scheme, the approach now was to design for the Games and review the proposals to be sure they did not contradict legacy requirements.

121 Sketch proposal for subdivision of International Broadcast Centre into separate buildings in legacy.

122 Early visualisation of public realm south of the Main Press Centre. This shows the intention of creating strong pedestrian links at the edges of the Park to neighbouring communities, in this case, Hackney Wick.

123 International Broadcast Centre. Exterior view across the Park. Panels of exterior cladding could be replaced by glazed units to suit different legacy uses.

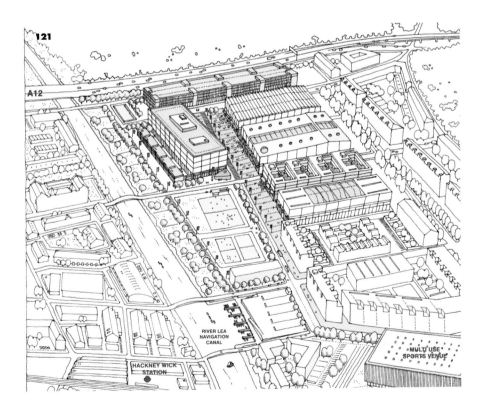

121

A12

RIVER LEA
NAVIGATION
CANAL

HACKNEY WICK
STATION

MULTI-USE
SPORTS VENUE

THE INTERNATIONAL BROADCAST CENTRE (IBC)

The IBC is 275m long by 104m wide by 21m tall, large enough to house five jumbo jets from wing-tip to wing-tip. The building has temporary planning permission and could undergo extensive change, depending on its legacy occupier(s). Its steel frame is easily adaptable and its structural design allows for the building to be sub-divided into three separate buildings.

> *'We were constantly applying a value-for-money judgement. Developers don't build for flexible futures because they can't predict the needs of future occupiers, and that's what we had to keep in mind. There was a constant balance to be struck between what was sensible to spend on flexibility and what wasn't.'*
>
> JEROME FROST, OLYMPIC DELIVERY AUTHORITY

Column spacing, floor-to-floor heights, floor loadings and servicing were designed to provide as much flexibility as possible within the budget, and BBC guidance was consulted to allow for television studios as one potential future use. The 13m-high ground floor required for Games has been designed so that intermediate floors can easily be introduced in legacy, and sections of the floor have been built so that they can be broken out and replaced. The intensive servicing plant required for cooling the studios during the Games is located on temporary external gantries that will be removed during Transformation.

THE MAIN PRESS CENTRE (MPC)

The four-storey MPC is a 29,000m² concrete-framed permanent building designed from the outset for offices. The building has flexible cores more suitable for start-up businesses than conventional corporate offices. Concrete soffits are exposed and conditioned air is supplied via a displacement system with chilled beams. A building was designed to meet the IOC's requirements for numbers of desks and briefing rooms, deeper than a conventional office floor plate. To make the building more flexible in legacy, the MPC has a two-storey projection, nicknamed 'the toe', which extends west towards Hackney Wick. The roof slab of this projection is designed so that a portion of it can be removed to create an atrium between 'the toe' and the main building, so that it can be subdivided for separate tenancies, creating a greater variety of lettable spaces and catering to a wider range of tenants.

MATERIALS

As part of CLM's requirement for an Environmental Manager on every site, BioRegional seconded a staff member as a sustainability advisor to Carillion for the IBC/MPC Complex project. Substitutions were made to the concrete and carpet specifications, and vigilant site supervision ensured that the ODA's requirement for 100 per cent FSC and PEFC-certified timber was met. The sustainability advisor held weekly meetings with the site workforce.

124 Aerial view of IBC/MPC Complex. The International Brodcast Centre is the largest building on the left, the permanent MPC is on the right, and the car park is in the foreground. The car park has been designed and constructed so that half of the building can be dismantled after the Games.

125 Early Carillion/Igloo Regneration legacy scheme for IBC/MPC Complex site. The quarter was envisioned as 'Soho East'. The International Brodcast Centre was to be subdivided into several smaller buildings with interior courtyards.

124

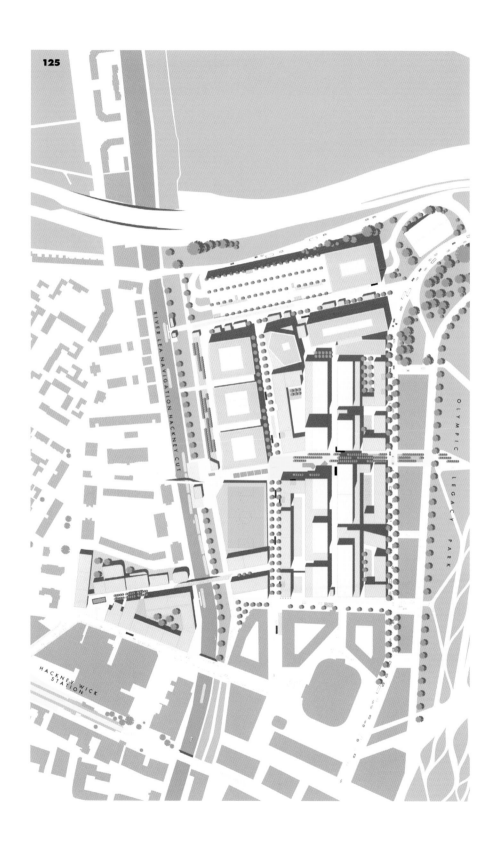

125

RIVER LEA NAVIGATION HACKNEY CUT

OLYMPIC LEGACY PARK

HACKNEY WICK STATION

'Everybody on site now knows what FSC timber is and the importance of capturing delivery notes. Two years ago they wouldn't have known. This is an important part of legacy learning.'

CHLOE SOUQUE, CARILLION SUSTAINABILITY ADVISOR (SECONDED FROM BIOREGIONAL)

On the MPC, a concrete mix with 30 per cent PFA and 100 per cent stent (a weathered aggregate that is a waste product from the china clay industry in Cornwall) was poured in all the cores and the ground floor slab; the typical 'London' mix being used across the site had only 50 per cent stent. The 100 per cent stent mix proved successful with no impact on the aspect of the concrete or the programme. Initial contractor scepticism was overcome, and the same mix was then used on the catering building and by Carillion on subsequent non-London 2012 buildings.

For the MPC's post-tensioned floor slabs, BioRegional recommended the use of a mix with 50 per cent GGBS and 100 per cent stent aggregate, based on their experience at FeildenCleggBradley's One Brighton, for which they were the developer. Although the project team was initially reluctant because the MPC slabs spanned 13m compared to only 7m at One Brighton, the mix was adopted and resulted in a 22 per cent reduction in embodied carbon in these slabs (compared to a conventional 100 per cent Portland Cement mix).

126 Exterior view of the Main Press Centre showing careful detailing of rainscreen cladding. The building has a 50 per cent glazing ratio and brise soleil on two façades.

127 Main Press Centre multi-storey car park. Visualisation in legacy with rooftop photovoltaic array that contributes a share of the Park's long-term renewable energy.

128 Interior view of studio inside the International Broadcast Centre.

Carpets was another area where close scrutiny resulted in environmental wins. Because of the large quantities involved, the carpet specification for both buildings was carefully reviewed. A loop carpet tile, which has less material content than cut pile, was selected from a manufacturer with a take-back scheme. The details of the manufacturer's recycling programme were examined to make certain that the tiles were recycled rather than downcycled.

Ensuring that all timber on the job met the ODA's certification requirement proved challenging on these buildings, as on many others across the Olympic Park site. Many subcontractors, even those with ISO 14001 certification, had never been required to provide paperwork as part of the audit trail for FSC certification. The primary uses of timber on the complex were for packaging (pallets for M&E parts, etc), concrete shuttering and doors.

Door specifications were examined to ensure that the cores, veneers and lippings were all FSC-certified, and a UK-manufactured door was selected over FSC-labelled doors from China and India because it was easier to ensure that all the parts of the door met the certifications. Even timber for pipe and duct supports and in toilet pod partitions was documented to meet the ODA's commitment for Park-wide timber certification.

AFTER THE GAMES

The sheer size of the press buildings has had two further important repercussions. When the wind turbine was dropped from the Eton Manor site, the entire Olympic Park was re-examined to see where renewables could be introduced. The MPC's 2,500m² roof makes it an ideal location for PVs. Detailed studies examined the extent of PVs that could be fitted without adversely impacting the biodiversity of the brown roof. The adjacent multi-storey car park will be fitted with PVs after the Games. Secondly, the complex, along with Westfield, is the largest potential employment generator in the Olympic Park site and could eventually house up to 10,000 new jobs. This employment base is critical to addressing the polarisation in Hackney between exclusive professional jobs on the City fringe and the 24 per cent of its population that is without formal qualifications. An important aspect of training and skills development will be working with local schools, colleges, Skills Councils and business organisations to develop vocational pathways for local residents.

Across the London 2012 construction programme, the most successful buildings have been those with a clear end use, like the Velodrome and the Handball Arena. With the IBC/MPC Complex's future tenancy not defined and sustainability as a key driver, the ODA's decision to build a flexible venue and hold costs down on the IBC has a clear logic.

The fact that almost 50 expressions of interest were received by the OPLC for the site with proposals for very different uses – creative, media, retail, cultural, education, leisure – is nonetheless encouraging, and the flexibility of the building should facilitate a legacy refurbishment that mitigates the monolithic nature of the buildings to make them more sympathetic neighbours to the future residential blocks in the Park. The main ongoing challenge will be the uncertainty of the market, particularly in the period immediately after the Games.

KEY POINTS
Flexibility for subdivision in legacy
Constraints of market demand
Strong environmental management on site

129 Interior view of International Broadcast Centre office space.

130 Main Press Centre. View of exposed concrete soffits and services distribution routes screened by open metal slats. Separate lighting and chilled beam components provide cost-effective flexibility for subsequent fit-out alterations.

131

Olympic and Paralympic Village

The story behind the Olympic and Paralympic Village is the most complex of the entire London 2012 project. After the Games, it will be converted to a high-density, mixed-tenure community with 2,800 new homes, a 50–50 mix of private and affordable housing, which will benefit from excellent proximity to public transport. It includes a school and a Polyclinic to broaden the mix of uses and serve the nearby existing community of Leyton. A quality public realm is critical to support the long-term sustainability of this new urban quarter of London.

131 The ODA deliberately selected a large variety of architects to design the Olympic and Paralympic Village housing so that each individual block would have its own identifiable character.

ENVIRONMENTAL PROFILE

Housing: Code for Sustainable Homes Level 4; BREEAM Communities – pilot project

CO_2 emissions reduction beyond Building Regulations Part L 2006: 82%

Reduction in potable water consumption: 33%

Recycled content (proportion of secondary materials as percentage of value): average 21%

Recycled aggregate (proportion of secondary materials as percentage of mass): average 28%

Percentage of raw materials delivered by rail: 85%

MATERIALS

Main materials: precast concrete

Materials with recycled content: concrete

Innovative approach: site-wide water attenuation strategy, ecological parkland

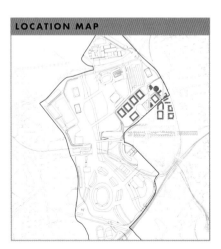

LOCATION MAP

Stratford City

What now comprises the Olympic and Paralympic Village was originally part of a larger 73ha masterplan for Stratford City prepared by Fletcher Priest Architects for development team Chelsfield Stanhope London and Continental Railways. The developers had assembled the site from former rail lands around Stratford station in anticipation of the area's improved transport connections with the arrival of the Channel Tunnel Rail Link (CTRL).

'Waiting for a City' is the revealing title of Swiss landscape architects Vogt's proposals for the Village and nearby Stratford. The project's genesis dates from 2002, prior to the London 2012 bid, and its first permanent residents will arrive only in 2013, after the athletes' apartments are transformed into flats.

The initial planning submission, which preceded the London 2012 bid, was primarily a retail scheme, but Newham lobbied hard for housing and mixed uses, and the project that emerged proposed high-density housing with a school alongside a major retail complex (now Westfield) and office buildings.

The Stratford project had an additional challenge as 2.5 million cubic metres of soil from the CTRL excavation had been deposited on the site, raising its level by approximately 6m above the surrounding streets. Although this facilitated bridging over the rail tracks and elevated the site above the floodplain, it made it difficult to integrate with the surrounding city.

When London won the Games and the site for the Olympic Park was located in the Lea Valley adjacent to the Stratford City proposal, the immediate pressure to accommodate 17,000 athletes and the compactness of the Olympic Park meant that the Olympic and Paralympic Village was assimilated into a portion of the Stratford City masterplan. The project that was eventually built resulted from protracted negotiation to adapt the previously approved Stratford City scheme to the new reality.

The housing is grouped into 11 courtyard plots over parking podiums, an unusual housing typology for London. An all-age educational academy and a Polyclinic will cater to residents of the Village and nearby Leyton. Due to the proximity of good public transport, planners agreed to a reduced parking provision from 0.7 to 0.5 per home. The site also includes six plots of undeveloped land with the potential for another 2,000 homes after the Games.

In 2007, Lend Lease joined with the Architecture Foundation to launch an international competition for the housing design. Almost 50 practices were shortlisted from over 400

ENVIRONMENTAL PROFILE

Housing: Code for Sustainable Homes Level 4; BREEAM Communities – pilot project

CO_2 emissions reduction beyond Building Regulations Part L 2006: 82%

Reduction in potable water consumption: 33%

Recycled content (proportion of secondary materials as percentage of value): average 21%

Recycled aggregate (proportion of secondary materials as percentage of mass): average of 28%

Percentage of raw materials delivered by rail: 85%

MATERIALS

Main materials: precast concrete

Materials with recycled content: concrete

Innovative approach: site-wide water attenuation strategy, ecological parkland

132 Olympic and Paralympic Village Housing. The precast concrete cladding replicates bas-reliefs from the Pantheon's Elgin Marbles. Twenty-five different panels create texture and variety on the 10-storey facade.

submissions, including many smaller practices. When the credit crunch hit the financial market a year later, Lend Lease was no longer able to take the project forward and the ODA stepped in with Lend Lease retained as project manager and Bovis Lend Lease as contractor. Ricky Burdett, who was Chief Design Advisor to the ODA during this period, highlighted the importance of a quality public realm for both Stratford City and the Olympic and Paralympic Village. Following a competitive process design company Vogt Landscape was appointed to lead on this aspect of the project.

URBAN PARKLANDS

The determination to avoid a gated new development that is isolated from surrounding communities underpinned the project from the outset. Parks and open space with major water features were the defining elements of the public realm. As the design developed, the open space was conceived as a permeable series of routes through the site with clearly defined spaces of different characters. The Village contains more than 10ha of open space, parks, public squares, communal gardens, courtyards and roof gardens.

The flood risk assessment for the Lea River Valley had established that water needed to be cleared from the site as quickly as possible in the event of a flood, so that it could be evacuated before more water arrived from upstream. Topography and water are used to shape what Vogt calls an 'ecologically informed' public realm that links the semi-rural

133 'Chassis' design for Olympic and Paralympic Village housing. A uniform system of structure, floor plates and cores was developed to achieve costs savings.

134 Olympic and Paralympic Village housing. Blocks, 10 to 12 storeys high, enclose generous courtyards.

135 Comparison of massing and street widths of Cadogan Gardens, Brompton with Olympic and Paralympic Village housing blocks.

133

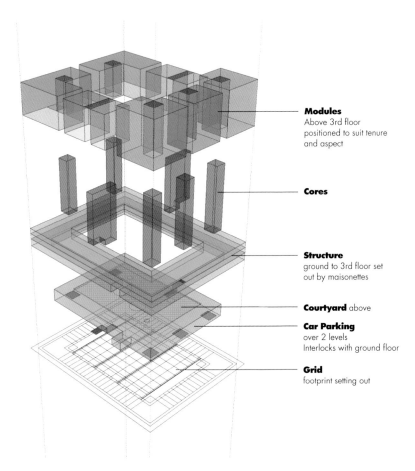

Modules
Above 3rd floor
positioned to suit tenure
and aspect

Cores

Structure
ground to 3rd floor set
out by maisonettes

Courtyard above

Car Parking
over 2 levels
Interlocks with ground floor

Grid
footprint setting out

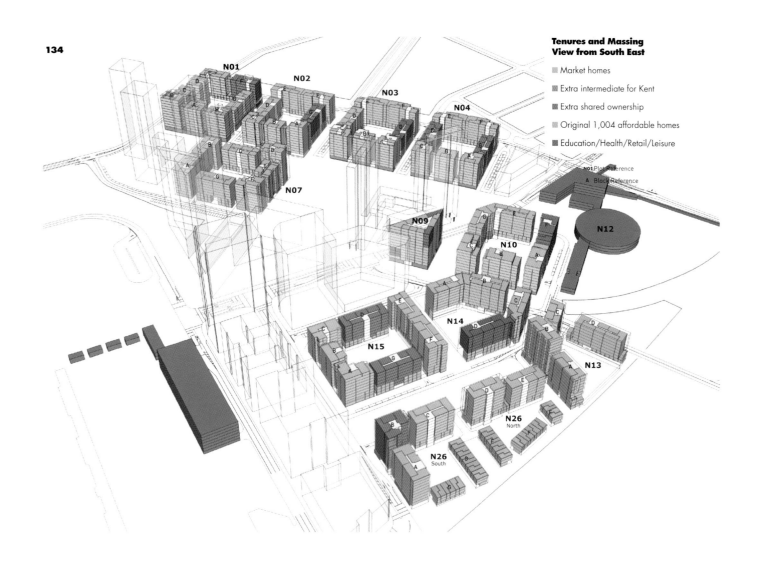

134

**Tenures and Massing
View from South East**

- Market homes
- Extra intermediate for Kent
- Extra shared ownership
- Original 1,004 affordable homes
- Education/Health/Retail/Leisure

N01 Plot Reference
A Block Reference

N01 N02 N03 N04 N07 N09 N10 N12 N14 N15 N13 N26 North N26 South

135

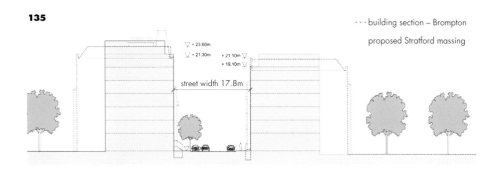

··· building section – Brompton

proposed Stratford massing

▽ + 23.60m
▽ + 21.30m
+ 21.10m ▽
+ 19.10m ▽

street width 17.8m

qualities of the Lea Valley to urban Stratford with a 7m-level change across the site. Changes in topography and informal planting define paths and enclosures, and a series of water features provide attenuation, rainwater storage and natural filtration as the site steps down to the River Lea. A non-potable water network supplied from the wetlands feeds the feature ponds and provides site-wide irrigation for the central open spaces and residential courtyards and grey water flushing for the school. This use of water to shape the urban design of the public realm on a project of this scale is new to the UK.

A NEW HOUSING TYPOLOGY FOR LONDON
Equally new to London were the proposed courtyard housing blocks, which are more akin to Barcelona's successfully adapted Athletes' Village on that city's waterfront than to London's own neighbourhoods of terraces and squares. Several drivers – primarily budget and programme – led to the adoption of standardised courtyard blocks as the preferred solution for the London 2012 Olympic and Paralympic Village – initially in heights ranging between 6 and 12 storeys. Housing wraps around landscaped courtyards with three-storey maisonettes at street level and flats above with a mix of private and affordable housing. This contrasted sharply with the four- to eight-storey housing envisioned to define the edges of the Olympic Park in Allies & Morrison's original masterplan.

To refine the housing design, residential masterplanning by Allford Hall Monaghan Morris (AHMM) analysed the grain and hierarchy of London neighbourhoods such as Marylebone

136 Masterplan for Stratford City prior to Olympic bid. A major water feature defined the public realm of the proposed housing. The new housing typology contrasts markedly with the residential terraces of Leyton immediately to the east. The Eastway cycle circuit, now the site of the Velodrome, is visible to the north.

and Maida Vale to inform the scheme. Typical London residential blocks with communal gardens, as well as street sections and elevations, were overlaid with proposals inherited from Stratford City and then translated into briefs for the residential buildings. Working with Patel Taylor, AHMM developed residential design guidelines that addressed proportions, relationships with streets and public spaces and degrees of public character, and looked at design principles on a street-by-street rather than only on a building-by-building basis.

With the advent of the financial crisis in 2008 and the immovable deadline of housing 23,000 athletes and officials during the Games, the housing blocks were simplified to a uniform 8 to 10 storeys for ease and speed of delivery during the Olympic and Paralympic phase of the project. A precast 'chassis' served as a structural framework and a unit quota was established for each plot.

As the masterplan builds out in future, the introduction of towers and family housing will provide greater variety.

ENVIRONMENTAL PERFORMANCE
The original planning application for Stratford City required the housing to meet the EcoHomes Very Good standard, and the overall energy strategy called for 10 per cent energy efficiency from buildings, 15 per cent from CHP and 3 per cent from renewables, significantly less stringent than ODA standards. Midway through the project, the Government

137 Masterplan for the Olympic and Paralympic Village. Refinement of the public realm led to the development of a variety and sequence of open spaces that link to the ecological corridor of the Lea River Valley. Each housing block was designed by a different architect to create visual variety.

138 Aerial view of one block of Olympic and Paralympic Village housing. Mixed-tenure blocks are built around garden courtyards over a parking podium. All flat roofs not occupied by plant equipment have extensive sedum roofs.

released the Code for Sustainable Homes (CSH), its flagship policy for reducing carbon emissions from new-build housing. The CSH has six levels, which each set specific targets for energy and water use.

The costs for the Village had to be revisited in light of the new CSH standard to determine which level of the code could realistically be met. The revised planning application called for CSH 3 with an aspiration for CSH 4. The ODA succeeded in upgrading the environmental performance standards that had been previously approved, and the project is the largest CSH 4 scheme built to date in the UK. The increase in wall insulation alone added approximately £8 million to the project value over an equivalent CSH Level 3 project. The entire Village is linked into the Olympic Park Energy Centre. Plot design guidelines specified U-values, shading and ventilation requirements for windows, taking account of 2050 climate data to address global warming.

139 Aerial view of the Olympic and Paralympic Village under construction. The financial crisis of autumn 2008 necessitated budget cuts and value engineering, which resulted in a uniformity in the block designs to enable economies of scale.

The Village sustainability team was particularly effective in documenting the audit process for certified timber by developing a quarterly reporting process with TRADA. The ODA subsequently adopted the Lend Lease approach to timber documentation. Procurement of lighting was another area where the Village led the way. Site-wide procurement enabled supplier Philips to bring new products to the market and also ensured the future-proofing of fittings for maintenance or replacement, particularly important in a sector of the market that is evolving very rapidly.

CHANGING FORTUNES AND MOVING TARGETS

In delivering the Village, ambitions that had been set in a pre-London 2012 Games world had to be rapidly adapted to deal with fixed time frame and certainty in the context of changing UK regulations on carbon reduction. Sensitivity to the vagaries of the market is endemic to all masterplanning, but in Stratford the complexity was compounded by the immovable deadline of summer 2012 together with more stringent environmental targets.

The challenge post-Games will be two-fold: to create social places of exchange between new residents and the surrounding community that ensure that the Village becomes integrated with the surrounding city and to ensure that the public realm and parklands are well maintained and developed as a resource for the wider community.

KEY POINTS

Ecological landscape that provides flood attenuation
'Compact city' approach with high-density housing near public transport
Largest Code for Sustainable Homes Level 4 scheme to date

140 Olympic and Paralympic Village housing. Detail view of concrete cladding panel cast with design scanned from the Parthenon's Elgin Marbles housed in the British Museum.

141 Olympic and Paralympic Village housing. Detail view of balcony with ceramic screens..

Chobham Academy

A new academy is located at the northern boundary of the Olympic and Paralympic Village, adjacent to the community of Leyton. Designed as a circular building 'with no back', the school will cater to both existing residents in nearby communities and the new families who move into the Village.

A COMMUNITY LANDMARK

Chobham Academy, one of two non-residential buildings in the Village, was seen as an urban landmark from its earliest inception. As members of the Stratford City Master Plan team prior to the London 2012 bid, Allford Hall Monaghan Morris (AHMM) likened a school on this prominent site to a church in London's Victorian housing estates. Citing precedents such as the Albert Hall and John Nash's All Souls Church, the architects imagined a building with special architectural qualities, a unique form and materials that would differentiate it from the surrounding housing. When the constraints of budget and programme precipitated the redesign of the Village housing, AHMM fought hard to retain the circular form of the academy's main building.

Chobham Academy will serve 1,800 students aged 3 to 19 with an anticipated 50–50 split between Village and Leyton residents. Academy places are allocated based on distance from the school, and therefore the school was located at the northern site boundary to maximize proximity to Leyton.

Comprised of three buildings, the academy includes a main building, a primary school with nursery accommodation and a specialist arts building that also serves the community. To accommodate the Academy's specialism in Literature and the performing arts, music and drama facilities and studio spaces are housed within the specialist building. This mix of activities catering to all ages on a single site is intended to create a community focus.

The school's three buildings front a new public square and define pedestrian paths through the site with a minimum of fences. A 95m-long Cor-ten bridge provides a secure route for students over Temple Mills Road to nearby sports fields.

DESIGNING FOR LEGACY WITHOUT AN END USER

During the Games, Chobham Academy will be used for administrative and security functions and provide a gym for the athletes. It will open to students only in 2013. This means that no headteacher was in place for consultation during design. AHMM embraced this challenge, designing the buildings to be as flexible as possible.

ENVIRONMENTAL PROFILE

BREEAM: Excellent (target)

CO_2 emissions reduction beyond Building Regulations Part L 2006: 40%

Materials: All A-C rated in the Green Guide, compliant with Lend Lease grey lists of undesirable materials and ISO 9001 and 14001 certified

Recycled content (proportion of secondary materials as percentage of value): 23%

Recycled aggregate (proportion of secondary materials as percentage of mass): 26% in slabs and 38% in foundations and substructure

U-values

walls: 0.30 W/m²K

roof: 0.20 W/m²K

floor slab: 0.20 W/m²K

glazing: 1.15 W/m²K

MATERIALS

Primary materials: concrete, aluminium curtain walling, precast cladding elements

Materials with recycled content: concrete, carpet, partitions

Innovative technologies: Earth tubes

142 Chobham Academy's circular form and regular cladding pattern mean that it can be subdivided in many different ways, increasing flexibility for unforeseen changes in use.

'A fundamental idea about the long-term sustainability of the school is the potential to re-imagine its uses. The arts building is essentially a sports building with some factory rooflights that gives you well-lit teaching spaces. It's always likely to be an educational building, but the building is designed in such a way that the programme could vary.'

SIMON ALLFORD, AHHM

The circular building is conceived as a highly flexible linear space wrapped around a central atrium. It can be adapted with entrances at any point, and parts can be closed down after hours to accommodate community use. Flexibility is also evident in the specialism building's changing rooms, which can be arranged to serve either the school or a community sports programme. Simon Allford of AHHM notes that, 'The vision for the circular building is that its division – the points at which you raise the partitions for the classrooms – is a movable feast. The module of our cladding allows increments to happen. It's like a highly tailored office building, but it has a certain landmark quality that means it should – in terms of long-term sustainability – endear itself to the community because it's a special building.'

DETAIL DESIGN

The school's most innovative environmental feature is a 5m-deep network of earth tubes that passively supply pre-conditioned fresh air to the main circular building and to the primary school. Full natural ventilation was not possible due to the number of air changes per hour required by Building Bulletins, and noise from the nearby rail line. Low-velocity fans at the back of the classrooms draw in fresh air through low-level attenuated air intakes that are formally expressed on the building exterior as cowls. Operable casements within each bay allow occupant control of windows.

143 Sketch view of Chobham Academy from Leyton. The building's circular form is intended as a school with no 'back', catering equally to the Olympic and Paralympic Village and the existing community of Leyton. The academy will have extensive playing fields; students will access the northern playing fields by a pedestrian bridge over the road.

144 View of Chobham Academy exterior. The roof will be accessible and roof planters will encourage gardening projects. Ventilation cowls with operable casements below create a rhythm on the facade.

145 Site plan of Chobham Academy. The round form of the secondary school building serves as an orienting landmark both for the Olympic and Paralympic Village and the adjacent community of Leyton which is part of the catchment area for the school.

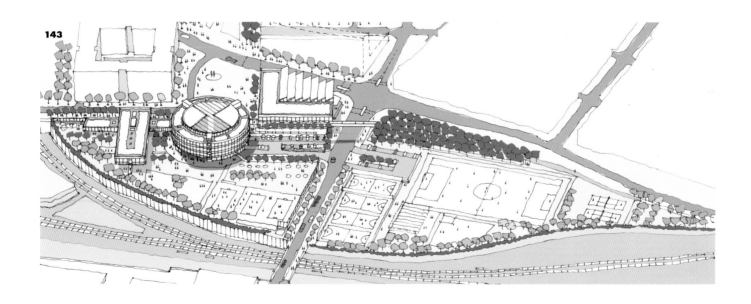

143

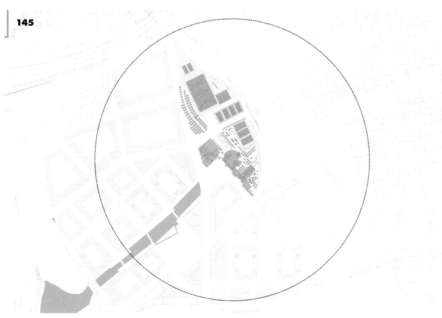

Green roofs have been incorporated in all three buildings: a meadow roof with a 120mm build-up on the primary school, a brown roof on the specialism building, and 2m-diameter planting troughs on the main building form part of a rooftop teaching area. The use of an ETFE roof over the circular atrium at the heart of the school allows plentiful daylight, reducing lighting loads. Provision has been made to add evacuated solar thermal tubes connected to the site-wide district energy system in future.

The building's concrete frame and soffits are exposed for thermal mass. The design team worked with London Concrete to maximise the use of recycled aggregates and cement substitutes in the concrete mixes, and with the contractor to ensure that formwork could be reused despite the main building's circular form. Rubber floors were specified throughout due to concerns about the phthalates in vinyl floors.

'A PLACE OF EXCHANGE'
Chobham Academy's ambition to provide a 'place of exchange' where the old and the new east London come together is full of promise. An all-age academy that co-locates a nursery, arts and sports facilities shared by the community, and adult learning on a single site has the potential for a broad reach. The specialism building, if well programmed and properly managed, could prove a strong draw. The disposition of the three buildings on the site makes for a highly permeable school that should facilitate community interaction.

KEY POINTS
Landmark building with distinctive form and materials
Building oriented to new housing in the Village and to Leyton
Earth tubes for conditioning building
Variety of green roofs incorporated where possible

146 View of green 'meadow' roof on the primary school building at Chobham Academy.

147 Site section of Chobham Academy showing how the stack effect helps draw air from the earth tubes into the buildings.

148 Site plan of Chobham Academy showing system of earth ducts that provide both heating and cooling to the building.

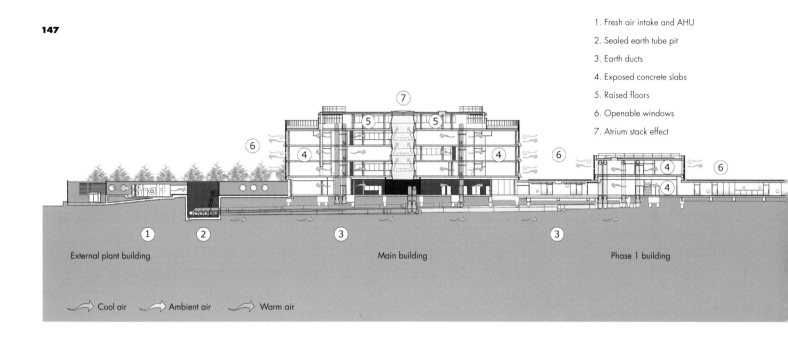

147

1. Fresh air intake and AHU
2. Sealed earth tube pit
3. Earth ducts
4. Exposed concrete slabs
5. Raised floors
6. Openable windows
7. Atrium stack effect

External plant building　　　　　Main building　　　　　Phase 1 building

⟶ Cool air　⟶ Ambient air　⟶ Warm air

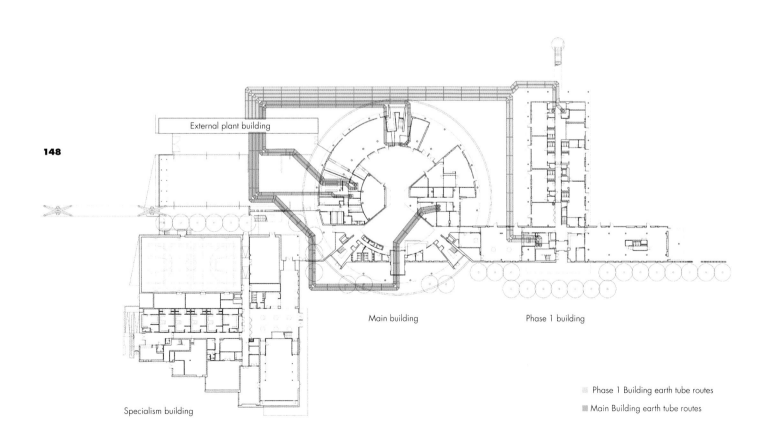

148

External plant building

Specialism building　　　Main building　　　Phase 1 building

▨ Phase 1 Building earth tube routes
▨ Main Building earth tube routes

Polyclinic

The Polyclinic is set on a triangular site at the north-eastern edge of the Olympic and Paralympic Village. It is designed to handle intensive use during the Games with flexibility built in to facilitate transformation to a community health building in legacy.

First-rate medical provision is essential for any Olympic and Paralympic Games, and is required by the IOC to treat common sports injuries and offer preliminary treatment before sending a seriously injured athlete to hospital. The medical facility also houses the crucially important anti-doping facilities throughout the Games.

SHARED COMMUNITY USE
As part of the Section 106 Agreement in the planning application for the Village, Lend Lease committed to build a Polyclinic whose post-Games catchment area would include Leyton. The Section 106 also stipulated that the clinic would house the offices of a Community Development Trust (CDT). Architects Penoyre & Prasad had to design a flexible legacy building suitable for LOCOG during the Games and the medical clinic and the CDT afterwards.

The clinic's prominent location on one of the main axial approaches from the Village makes the building visible from afar. In a gesture towards the Village, a sweeping prow-like roof increases the presence of this relatively small 5,000m² building, which the architects liken to 'a little church amongst Manhattan's skyscrapers'. A double-height arcade creates a welcoming street presence, and the entrance leads to an atrium shared by the clinic and the CDT, which is intended to occupy about a third of the building.

FUTURE-PROOFING
Newham Primary Care Trust (NPCT) was identified as the building's end user and developed a primary care brief including GP and physiotherapy offices and diagnostic and scanning rooms. Future-proofing was the key driver in the design of the four-storey building. Community offices could be transformed into additional clinic space or vice versa as needed.

> *'We know that if we fix a design in 2010, NPCT's idea of what they need inb 2013 will be quite different.'*
>
> MARK ROWE, PENOYRE & PRASAD

A shallow floor plate of approximately 13m is key, with regular fenestration so that internal partitions can be easily reconfigured. Rigour in the façade design means that if an internal partition moves by a metre, each internal space will still have one or two windows and the correct daylight factor. Services run down the middle of a double-loaded corridor and can

ENVIRONMENTAL PROFILE
BREEAM: Excellent (target)

CO_2 emissions reduction beyond Building Regulations Part L 2006: 33.1% (design BER)

Reduction in potable wat 36%

Percentage of materials with recycled content: N/A

U-values

walls: 0.2 W/m²K

roof: 0.14 W/m²K

floor: 0.2 W/m²K

glazing: 1.6 W/m²K

MATERIALS
Primary materials: concrete, brick

Recycled materials: aggregate in *in situ* concrete

Innovative technologies and approaches: R290 gas chillers

The Polyclinic is designed to handle intensive use during the Games with flexibility built in to facilitate transformation to a community health building in legacy.

149 View of Polyclinic interior atrium, which will be a shared space between the health clinic and a community development trust, catering to residents of both the Olympic and Paralympic Village and Leyton.

easily be reconfigured. Despite the shallow floor plate, natural ventilation proved impossible for acoustic reasons due to the proximity of adjacent railway lines.

Other environmental features include a sedum roof and the harvesting of rainwater for toilet flushing. The ODA's requirement for a full audit trail for FSC and PEFC certification ruled out the use of composite windows, so aluminium windows were specified throughout. Gas chillers that use hydrocarbon refrigerant R-290 with low global warming potential were specified as the most energy-efficient approach to cooling, and energy-efficient blade hand dryers are used in all the toilets.

Predicted annual CO_2 emissions for the building are $18.5kg/m^2$, lower than the $25kg/m^2$ Penoyre & Prasad have averaged on a recent string of health buildings, due to the impact of the district heating. Features such as sedum roofs and rainwater harvesting that are regularly value-engineered out when budgets are tight were retained here due to the overall environmental ambition of the project.

150 An arcade along the south-facing street frontage of the Polyclinic provides a welcoming entrance and solar shading.

151 The sweeping roof form is a gesture towards the Olympic and Paralympic Village.

152 Sketch aerial view. The Polyclinic is designed to be highly flexible for end user Newham Primary Care Trust. A shallow 13m-deep floor plate and regular fenestration mean that interior partitions can be easily relocated.

The eventual appeal of this building will depend greatly on how the community occupancy plays out. Empty tenancies alongside the health clinic would be detrimental to both the streetscape and the atrium. The small-scale community activities emerging west of the Park in Bromley-by-Bow suggest that something similar could also happen here.

Legacy is king in this project, and the Village and Leyton will inherit an inviting well-designed health facility. LOCOG is the short-term beneficiary during the Games.

KEY POINTS

Legacy catchment area Village and Leyton
Community-facing brief – Community Development Trust
Future-proofing – flexible plan

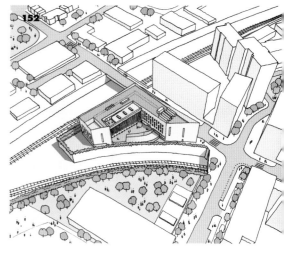

Chapter 4

The Overlay

The overlay (created by Populous with Allies & Morrison and Lifschutz Davidson Sandilands) is a central element of the Games because it makes the most of London's historical settings for use as sporting venues. Seating stands and accommodation from the hire market are used to create temporary venues with well-known views of London as a backdrop. LOCOG has capitalised on the English summer tradition of garden parties with tents and marquees to create a festival atmosphere rooted with a strong sense of place, overcoming the potential anonymity of repetitive hired components. The more that can be hired, the more that can be easily returned to the rental market after the Games, thereby reducing carbon and waste.

STAGING THE GAMES – THE 'OVERLAY'

Overlay is a term from the events industry for everything of an event-specific nature that is required to stage the Olympic and Paralympic Games. Thirteen existing venues across London and 10 across the UK will be dressed for the Games. On some sites, this involves primarily back of house (BOH) installations, while at some of London's historic venues, such as the Beach Volleyball stands at Horse Guards Parade and the Equestrian platform at Greenwich Park, it is everything. Wherever possible, London's historic settings will be used as stage sets. The Mall will be used as start and finish of the Marathons and Olympic Cycling Road Races; Hyde Park will host the Triathlon finish and 10km Marathon Swimming; and Road Cycling will take place at The Mall and Hampton Court Palace. Historic sports venues, including Wimbledon and Lord's Cricket Ground, as well as existing arenas and convention centres, will all be put to use in keeping with the strategy of building new permanent venues only when there is a community benefit or operational need in legacy.

The amount of overlay is extensive, and covers all of the BOH accommodation for new, temporary and existing venues, including sponsors' concessions, catering facilities, security infrastructure and temporary power. LOCOG is procuring approximately 200,000 temporary seats, 250,000m^2 of tents and 4,000 cabin units. Overlay also includes the temporary dressing that will help create the look and feel of the Games and will dramatically impact public perception about the environmental achievements of the Games. To increase public awareness of the Games' sustainability agenda, state-of-the-art smart metering will be installed in the Olympic and Paralympic Village.

Inspired by the longstanding British tradition of tents at flowers shows and rowing regattas, one of the largest overlay installations will be at the Village. Lifschutz Davidson Sandilands' design proposes a giant encampment of a multitude of small tents with 10m-spans, topped with colourful shading devices, to retain a human scale and add visual interest to a repetitive installation. The intention is to capture the flavour of an English garden party with extensive planting in temporary pots and screens.

1 (Previous page) Aerial view of Equestrian test event at Greenwich Park, July 2011. The Arena from the test event will be reused at the Games and can be reused numerous times. It is designed so that it does not penetrate the ground.

2 A club runner races down The Mall towards the finishing line at the test event for the London 2012 Olympic Marathon. The iconic backdrop of Buckingham Palace brings a sense of pageantry and spectacle to the occasion.

DESIGN DEVELOPMENT

LOCOG developed a strategic approach to the sustainability aspects of the overlay and challenged conventional Games practice by inspiring designers to develop sustainable approaches to overlay design. Carbon footprint modelling established early on that the majority of carbon emissions was in the embodied carbon of the materials rather than in the power required during the Games. LOCOG developed Temporary Materials Guidelines in collaboration with Atkins and other stakeholders in early 2010 that focused LOCOG sustainability initiatives in four areas: reduce to a minimum the amount of materials and embodied carbon in the overlay, hire a maximum of components from the rental market, specify the afterlife of any remaining materials and work with sponsors to improve the sustainability of their supply chains.

To rationalise the approach and achieve efficiencies of hireable and reusable elements, LOCOG commissioned Populous to develop a Kit of Parts for the overlay. It is comprised of over 86 components that can be combined in different ways. This excerpt from the section on boundaries and fencing is indicative of LOCOG's approach:

‘We made every effort to work with standard
sizes and configurations and avoid over-specifying
and bespoking.’

PHIL CUMMING, LOCOG CORPORATE SUSTAINABILITY MANAGER

‘Standard components are employed wherever possible or, if new elements are required,
they are designed to be reusable by the industry. Waste is minimised with zero landfill; and
materials [should be] suitable for reuse rather than recycling. Flexibility is provided by use of
the standard module allowing for late additions or subtractions as demands vary.’

It is worth noting the emphasis on reuse rather than simply recycling, a ‘lesson learned’ from
the demolition process on the Olympic Park site (see p. 52).

Helped by the UK’s temperate climate, LOCOG also challenged the conventional assumption
that all tents would require cooling. By carefully matching temporary uses with the
appropriate portable cabins or tents and scrutinising ventilation requirements for each one,
over 70 per cent of non-essential comfort cooling was eliminated.

3 Equestrian test event at Greenwich Park, July
2011. The embodied carbon of four different
structural options for the Equestrian platform
was calculated and evaluated along with
other design considerations. The logs used in
the jumps are FSC-certified.

4 Plan of Greenwich Park: Equestrian Arena
(orange) and back of house accommodation
(black). The park was mapped including
tree and tree root locations so that all
accommodation and vehicular movement
could be planned to avoid damage to trees.

5 (Overleaf) Aerial view of Equestrian test
event at Greenwich Park, July 2011.

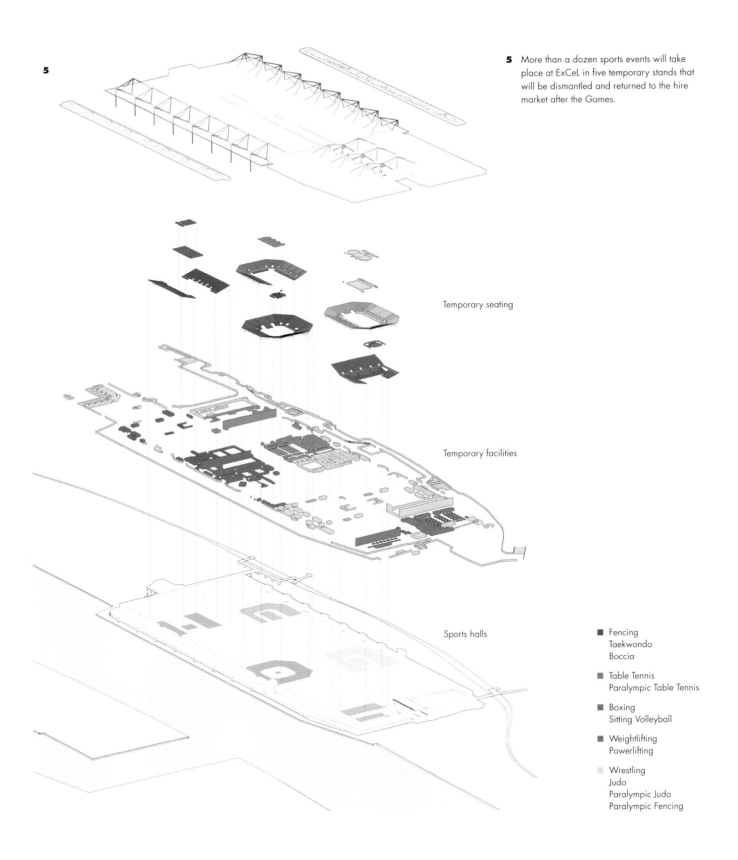

5

5 More than a dozen sports events will take place at ExCeL in five temporary stands that will be dismantled and returned to the hire market after the Games.

Temporary seating

Temporary facilities

Sports halls

■ Fencing
Taekwondo
Boccia

■ Table Tennis
Paralympic Table Tennis

■ Boxing
Sitting Volleyball

■ Weightlifting
Powerlifting

■ Wrestling
Judo
Paralympic Judo
Paralympic Fencing

6 London 2012 made extensive use of temporary stands, including the Aquatics Centre's temporary wings. The steel structure, seating stands and wrap will be dismantled for reuse or recycling after the Games.

OVERLAY – LOCOG'S PRIORITY SUSTAINABILITY TARGETS

— Hire 85% per cent of all overlay commodities

— Reduce physical footprint of LOCOG venues by 25% against 2006 baseline

— Reduce non-essential comfort cooling (HVAC) by 70% against 2008 baseline

— Purchase 20% of materials (by value) with recycled content or from secondary source

— Reuse or recycle 90% (by weight) of materials arising from overlay.

7

1. Olympic Stadium

2 Aquatics Centre

3. Water Polo

4. Handball Arena

5. IPC/MBC

6. Hockey Centre

7. Eton Manor

8. Velodrome

9. BMX Track

10. Basketball Arena

11. Olympic and Paralympic Village

12. Chobham Academy

13. Polyclinic

14. Olympic Hospitality Centre (sponsored)

15. Energy Centre

16. Primary Substation

■ Permanent building

■ Overlay

This approach of re-examining fundamental assumptions during early design stages and questioning the practice of designing to worst case scenarios is an important aspect of delivering lower carbon solutions. In a similar vein, LOCOG was able to persuade Building Control to extend the 30-day definition of temporary for the duration of the Games, so that overlay accommodation – most of which will be installed for approximately 10 weeks – could be classified as temporary. To the extent possible, ODA site cabins are being reused and new cabins are being procured in standard sizes to minimise bespoke solutions.

Following the lead of Populous' Stadium design, LOCOG 'embraced the temporary' for much of the overlay. All Games-time installations, from lighting to tree planting, were evaluated to determine whether they were strictly necessary and whether they could remain post-Games.

Where commodities are purchased rather than hired, reuse options have been explored. Over 2,000 tonnes of sand purchased for the London Prepares Series Beach Volleyball test event at Horse Guards Parade in 2011 was donated to four London sports venues within a

7 Plan showing permanent buildings (grey) and temporary overlay (brown) at the Olympic Park. Extensive use of overlay can be seen at the Eton Manor site, at the Basketball Arena and Hockey Centre in the northern part of the Park and at the Olympic Hospitality Centre for sponsors north of the Water Polo Arena. LOCOG and the ODA collaborated so that the majority of tree planting, which normally would happen only after the Games, was coordinated with the overlay so that more tree planting could take place before the Games.

8 Temporary stands for Beach Volleyball test event at Horse Guards Parade, July 2011. The use of historic London as a backdrop provides visual drama which means that the stands themselves can be kept to a minimum. Sand from the test events was distributed to local sports centres.

8

9

16km radius of the site to create seven new courts to promote the sport. A similar approach will be taken after the Games. Used tennis balls will be donated to local clubs, and those that cannot be reused will be turned into nests for dormice!

Supply chain engagement has also driven innovation. Because of the quantities required, LOCOG worked with portable toilet supplier Elliott to bring to market new eco-toilet units with waterless urinals, low-flow taps and low-energy hand dryers. The key lesson is that performance specification with resiliency in procurement can lead to more sustainable solutions. This was a fundamental part of the lighting strategy for the Park where the desire to provide an integrated solution led to single procurement through a single manufacturer.

LOCOG has engaged project teams through workshops at regular intervals to review sustainability requirements at each design stage, and document actions and ideas for the next stage. A sustainability working group reviews each package of work, drilling down into detailed issues such as toxicity of materials and any alternative products on the market, potential for increasing recycled content, and travel distances for core suppliers. All lighting was reviewed to ensure that highly energy-efficient products were specified that still met broadcasting requirements.

The structural studies for Allies & Morrison's Equestrian platform at Greenwich Park illustrate

the complexities of sustainability tradeoffs involved in overlay design. The 110m by 90m platform must be extremely stable to suit the horses and leave no trace in the park's heritage landscape when removed. Structural engineer Atkins compared four solutions: expanded polystyrene (EPS) blocks, steel frame with a timber deck, steel frame with precast planks and compacted fill. After extensive testing by LOCOG to ensure there would be no disturbance to the horses, the steel frame and timber deck build-up has been selected as the preferred option. It was also the most sustainable, containing the lowest amount of embodied energy in materials and requiring the fewest number of lorry trips.

Other initiatives at Greenwich Park include the establishment of a local riding school at Shooters Hill as a legacy of London 2012. All sand, like that at Horse Guards Parade, will be reused. All trees and their roots have been mapped, sensitive tree roots have been covered with woodchips and emergency vehicle routes have been planned to avoid tree damage. Used horse jumps have been sourced from previous equestrian events, and all logs used in jumps are FSC-certified timber. Approximately 100 bird and bat boxes are being located throughout Greenwich Park and low-density lighting is used to avoid disturbance to bats.

Box Hill, a National Trust property in Surrey's North Downs, will form part of London 2012's Cycling Road Race circuit. Because Box Hill is a designated Site of Special Scientific Interest (SSSI) and a Special Area of Conservation (SAC), protection of its natural environment

9 Entirely temporary, the Basketball Arena exemplifies London 2012's extensive use of overlay, which is more than double (in square metres) the amount used in each of the past three Olympic Games.

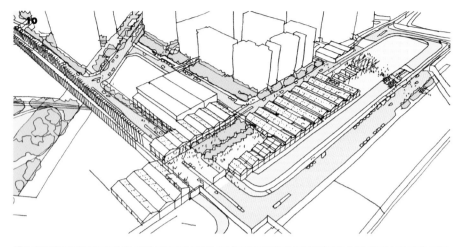

during the races is critical. LOCOG worked with the National Trust to carry out detailed ecological assessments of both flora and fauna at Box Hill in order to plan how to safeguard the most sensitive habitats. During the test events in summer 2011, over 3km of fencing were installed to enclose the more vulnerable areas, which were further protected by stewards specifically employed by LOCOG for the event. A similar approach will be used at the Games.

LOCOG's six sustainability partners – BMW, BP, BT, Cisco, EDF Energy and GE – will sponsor 'a walk in the park', a series of hubs that tell the sustainability story of the Olympic Park. LOCOG is working with Coca-Cola and BioRegional to develop a sustainability project in the Olympic and Paralympic Village that is part-funded by Defra. LOCOG has no precedent to follow on working with sustainability sponsors in the Games context, because this is the first time such work is being done. With this range of initiatives, LOCOG has set

a new benchmark in sustainable event management, including the development of a new British Standard – BS 8901:2009 for the events sector, which is currently being adapted internationally (ISO 20121).

London 2012's overlay strategy is one of its most far-reaching sustainability achievements. LOCOG's innovative approach to design and sourcing are at the crux of this success. The maximum use of existing venues and elements from the hire market has dramatically reduced both carbon and waste. Procurement packages with obligatory take-back clauses and careful scrutiny of the end use of any remaining materials has further contributed to waste reduction.

Chapter 5

Lasting Benefits

Legacy, the driving tenet of London 2012, is also the hardest to assess ahead of or even immediately post-Games. City-building is a question of decades, not months or even years. Yet many physical design initiatives already in place lay the groundwork for the principles of the Olympic Park to take hold in the surrounding communities. The most immediate tell-tale signs will be who is frequenting the Park in three to five years' time.

AFTER THE GAMES – 2012 AND BEYOND

When the Paralympic Games draw to a close, a contaminated site with a mix of local industry and a handful of vibrant community uses –such as the Lee Valley Cycle Circuit, allotments and weekend flea markets – will have been replaced by a new urban park that embodies the latest twenty-first-century environmental thinking. The removal of the blue perimeter fence that ringed the Games in and the community out for more than five years will open physical links between previously disconnected communities on either side of the Lea Valley.

Five sports venues will remain:
— a Stadium that will host football, athletics and a range of other sporting, cultural and
   community events including the IAAF 2017 World Championships;
— Zaha Hadid's Aquatics Centre – liberated from its temporary stands – with one of
   London's few 50m swimming pools;
— The Handball Arena – a flexible multi-use arena for community sports and events;
— a VeloPark, formed by the Velodrome with its indoor track, and a variety of outdoor
   cycling circuits for BMX, mountain biking and road cycling;
— and a community sports centre at Eton Manor.

1 (Previous page) Visualisation of Olympic Village in legacy. View of ten to twelve story blocks with public realm water features, looking towards the City.

2 New waterside picnic area at Three Mills accessible from the Fatwalk (left).

The Olympic and Paralympic Village's 50–50 mix of private and affordable housing will provide the seeds of a new residential community with just over 2,800 units in 2013, and potential for 2,000 on adjacent sites. The all-age Chobham Academy will primarily serve the Village at primary level, with a 50–50 intake from Village families and existing Leyton residents at secondary level, once established. The Polyclinic will also to serve both new and existing communities and house the offices of a local community trust.

Approximately £300 million and a year of construction will transform the Park immediately after the Games, work undertaken by the Olympic Park Legacy Company. Temporary venues, concourses and bridge decks will be dismantled and back of house accommodation and security infrastructure will be removed. Loop service roads will be connected to the local street network, and approximately 5km of cycle paths and footpaths will be completed. The 3.5m temporary widening of the Greenway for the Games will be removed, restoring the path to its 4m width. Over 2ha of allotments will be created in two plots, one at Eton Manor and one near Stratford, to replace those previously on the site. The Orbit will open after the Games, providing a significant new landmark and drawing visitors to the Park. Numerous 'stitches', London 2012 lingo for welcoming pedestrian connections, will be created between the Park and adjoining neighbourhoods to encourage people to use the Park and immediately establish a positive public perception of the Park as secure and inviting. To alleviate the barrenness of the many vacant sites that will remain immediately after the Games, interim landscaping will be planted along the boundaries of future development sites at key locations. Approaches from the surrounding neighbourhoods will be improved by removing physical barriers, widening and resurfacing pedestrian paths and improving underpasses and bridges with lighting and CCTV. All of these measures are intended to create a network of well-used paths where residents and visitors alike can orient themselves easily in this newly created piece of city.

3. The Olympic Park sits within the Lea River Park, which will be a major new open space for Londoners, created by the transformation of a working landscape into public space. The backbone of the park is the Fatwalk, an extra-wide footpath that stretches from Three Mills to East India Dock Basin, passing through the Olympic Park.

3

Stratford Causeway

Three Mills Green

Mill Meads & Abbey Mills

Twelve Trees

Working River

Poplar River Park

Exotic Wild

East India Dock Basin

4

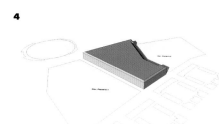

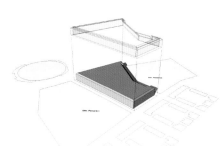

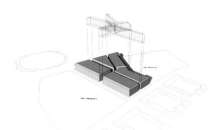

Step 1: establish Development Parcel boundaries and massing envelope from Parameter Plans

Step 2: apply principal street corridor dimensions and frontage offsets according to Parameter Plans and Design Codes

Step 3: establish required nuber of subdivisions within the Parcel using corridor dimensions associated with tertiary streets in accordance with Parameter Plans and Design Codes

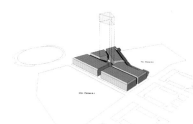

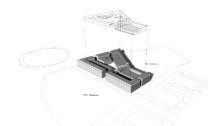

Step 4: define number and size and location of neighbourhood open space(s) in accordance with Parameter Plans and Design Codes

Step 5: define maximum frontage heights to tertiary streets and neighbourhood spaces in accordance with ratios as stated in the Design Codes

Step 6: define building sizes (width and depth) according to schedule of building types and relationship to public realm indicated in the Design Codes

Step 7: confirm maximum building widths and location of non-residential uses in accordance with Parameter Plans and Design Codes

Step 8: define built form and location of entrances/access to frontages in accordance with Design Codes

When transformation works are complete, the OPLC will turn the Velodrome and Eton Manor over to legacy manager Lee Valley Regional Park Authority. The parklands, the energy infrastructure, the Olympic Stadium, the Aquatics Centre, the Handball Arena and the two media buildings will also be turned over to the OPLC. A proposal to convert the OPLC to a Mayoral Development Corporation (MDC) in 2012 is a welcome initiative that would centralise more wide-reaching powers over the future development of the Olympic Park in a single municipal body. The OPLC will also be responsible for the ongoing relationship with Cofely and exploring alternatives for a lower carbon or renewable fuel solution for the Energy Centres. The London Development Agency and the London Thames Gateway Development Corporation have funded the extension of the Olympic Park district heating system's hot water pipe network to Stratford High Street to serve future developments with a view to further extensions to Bromley-by-Bow and Sugar House Lane. A search for a site for a syngas plant is ongoing so that the CHP network could run on lower carbon fuel.

4   The Housing Design Code for Legacy Masterplan, 2011, establishes guidelines for massing, street widths, frontage offsets, neighbourhood open spaces, maximum building widths, location of entrances and non-residential uses and landscape.

A major question mark remains over how rigorously the OPLC will be able to adhere to the ODA's ambitious sustainability agenda when it comes to the Stadium refurbishment, new housing and reuse of the press buildings. Unlike the ODA, which had a fixed timescale and a cleared ring-fenced site, the OPLC will be subject to the demands of the market.

EARLY DAYS AFTER THE GAMES

London parks as diverse as Regent's Park and Clapham Common illustrate how important edges are in defining an urban park. As custodian for the building out of the many remaining development sites, the OPLC (or future MDC) will play a critical role in shaping the character of the urban fabric around the future Queen Elizabeth Olympic Park. The Olympic Park legacy masterplan has gone through several iterations seeking to balance urban design and housing delivery with market demand. The current Olympic Park legacy masterplan calls for an additional 8,000 units of new housing, envisaged primarily as terraced housing for families. Housing design guidelines developed by Allies & Morrison address issues such as massing, setbacks and proportions of openings as well as environmental performance. Initial design proposals for these new urban quarters bode well for sustainable place making.

A terrace of family housing is proposed to front onto the Park and screen the IBC. Its enormous size, which together with the MPC comprises almost 90,000m^2 of potential commercial space, poses a considerable challenge. Depending on market interest, the IBC could be subdivided into three or four smaller blocks with streets running between them. A tipping point should come if a large anchor tenant leases a significant portion of one of the buildings. The intention is to accommodate creative digital industries in a range of studios, workshops and offices. When fully operational, the former media buildings, the venues and ongoing Park maintenance are anticipated to create up to 8,000 new jobs.

In the immediate post-Games period, it is the £1.45bn Westfield Stratford City development that will provide a major concentration of activity and employment, creating up to 8,500 jobs. Opened in autumn 2011, the 175,000 square metre project contains more than 300 shops and restaurants, including anchor tenants John Lewis and Marks & Spencer.

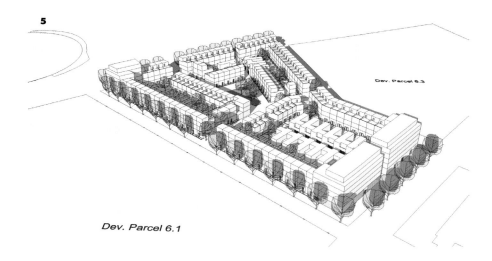

5

Dev. Parcel 6.3

Dev. Parcel 6.1

5 Housing Design Code for Legacy Masterplan, 2011. Landscape completes the public realm.

6 (Overleaf) Exterior view of the Velodrome set in the landscaped Olympic Park.

THE OLYMPIC PARK 'FRINGE'

7

The discontinuous urban fabric of large industrial sites severed by waterways and transportation and utilities infrastructure that characterised the Olympic Park site prior to redevelopment also extends to much of the surrounding area. To make the most of the regenerative potential of the Games on the wider area, the Mayor, simultaneously with preparation of the London 2012 bid in 2004, initiated an Opportunity Area Planning Framework that was adopted in 2007. It set out strategic guidance for land uses in the Lower Lea Valley, including employment centres, open space, transport links, retail concentration and areas of family housing. At the same time, the London Thames Gateway Development Corporation developed the Lower Lea Valley Vision focused on four key themes: extending the landscape spine of the Lee Valley Regional Park through the Olympic Park south to the Thames, reinforcement of existing and creation of new town centres, retention of industrial land and employment centres, and strengthened wayfinding and pedestrian links in the public realm.

Proposals for the Lower Lee Valley by architectural design practice 5th Studio, jointly commissioned by the London Thames Gateway Development Corporation, Design for London and the Lee Valley Regional Park Authority, are amongst the most compelling of all the design work in and around the Olympic Park. Like the landscape design for the Olympic Park, it is underpinned by a thorough understanding of the ecology of the valley, but it also takes the area's post-industrial overlay as a point of inspiration rather than sanitising it out. This work identified strategic interventions that were necessary to repair the urban fabric, restore key pedestrian links and facilitate wayfinding. The first phase of this work is the £28 million Fatwalk, a path that links Hackney Marshes to the Thames and like the Greenway (p. 16) has an explicit environmental agenda to encourage walking and cycling and reinforce the green spine of the Lea River Valley. The popularity of New York's High Line is an indicator that this type of landscaped walk can become a destination as well as a link.

Design for London (DfL) has taken a proactive role on urban design initiatives throughout the Lea Valley's public realm, commissioning six Olympic Fringe Masterplans as early as 2006 to assess the patchwork of neighbourhoods around the Olympic Park. DfL's strategic partners for the Fringe Masterplans include the Host Boroughs, the London Thames Gateway Development Corporation, the GLA and TfL, and each masterplan has a different design team.

Investment was prioritised to determine what was critical to deliver prior to the Games, immediately following the Games and in the longer term. The ambition is to create a connected piece of city. 'A big touchstone for us was Canary Wharf and seeing the impact of the severance between the DLR, and the no man's land between Poplar and Canary Wharf,' notes Eleanor Fawcett, Design for London. 'The levels of deprivation in Poplar have not changed 25 years on. It was thought of as an inward-looking, closed development. We want to ensure that that does not happen here, but the default setting is that it is likely to happen. [Our work aims to] make the town centres functional with places of exchange where new and existing communities can overlap and to locate primary schools and parks so that they're shared.'

Approximately £80 million will have been invested in public realm projects prior to the Games. High Street 2012 is another initiative that aims to strengthen the vehicular and pedestrian route from the City of London east to Stratford. These surgical interventions in the urban fabric remove existing physical barriers, widen and resurface pedestrian paths and improve the area's countless bridges and underpasses to facilitate crossing the A12, railway lines and the waterways. Although the public realm projects do not have specific environmental agendas or targets, they aim to encourage people to walk and cycle, thereby developing less carbon-intensive lifestyles. A new signage system throughout the area is part of a wayfinding strategy to help orient both local residents and visitors in this rapidly changing urban environment. This investment in the public realm is about creating a livelier, more diverse and better-connected city.

THE GAMES IS ONLY THE BEGINNING

From central Government to the Mayor's office to the Host Boroughs, the *raison d'être* behind the London 2012 bid has been regeneration. An improved public realm is a critical first step towards shaping the development that will take place as market forces, spurred by the London 2012 investment and by Westfield, start to impact the future character of the Lower Lea Valley. Connectivity opens up new employment opportunities and improves access to community facilities.

But physical change alone will not bring about the desired transformation. As a first step, the programming of sports activities and other uses that cater to the surrounding communities is needed to make the most of the Park's potential and ensure that it becomes a valued vibrant asset. Equally important, cross-borough cooperation is required to coordinate investment in job training, community partnerships, and local entrepreneurship so that new employment opportunities are generated hand in hand with physical change.

7 Hackney Marshes Centre, 2010. As part of the Olympic Fringe Delivery Programme, the LDA and Design for London worked with the LB Hackney to deliver a new sports and education facility for Hackney Marshes which forms a gateway to Eton Manor and the Olympic Park beyond.

8 Waterworks River with Olympic Stadium beyond. This view of a footpath along the Waterworks River is indicative of how the Olympic and Paralympic Games have transformed the formerly abandoned waterways of the Lea River Valley. This particular footpath will not be open to the public until after the Games.

8

9

ASSESSING THE SUSTAINABILITY
OF LONDON 2012

The message is clear. No longer can sustainability be tacked on as an afterthought at the end of the design process; nor can it be pigeon-holed as a technical concern for the project architect and service engineers. London 2012 has impacted that tendency by making sustainable design a driver from the outset.

London 2012 has fostered innovation in low carbon design in ways too numerous to count, but the Games' greatest achievement is the litmus test of legacy that has been applied to each venue and every procurement contract, adding a new dimension to the meaning of a sustainable built environment.

This broad-based approach has penetrated every aspect of design and construction. An understanding of the natural environment and the ecosystems indigenous to the Lea Valley underlies the design of the Park, but its role as a bridge and connector that enhances proximity to transport infrastructure and community facilities is equally critical. Walkable neighbourhoods are the cornerstone of a sustainable city.

9 Commissioned by the London Development Agency to replace a facility demolished as part of the Olympic programme, the Chandos Road Community Centre offers pre-school and after-school care. The building has a super-insulated breathing wall system, as well as ground source heat pumps and a green roof.

10 The momentum of London 2012 sparked a proposal for a solar lift to make the steep Duke of York steps accessible to all. Completion 2013.

Early engagement with environmental charities WWF and BioRegional imbued London's bid document with the compelling concept of a One Planet Olympic Games that would respect the environment. It could easily have stopped there. To deliver sustainable design, lip service is not enough. Working to specific budgets and an immovable deadline, the ODA and LOCOG translated these early aspirations into priority themes and from there into target metrics.

Quantitative targets are essential, but they must be tailored to their context. It is no use simply replicating London's targets in Rio because sustainability is a journey. Rio faces pressing problems of social inequity, poor transport and utility infrastructure, and an urgency to protect its natural environment that differentiate it from London. Every project, whether an Olympic Park or a single house, has a specific context and a different set of parameters. Even during the seven-year life of the London 2012 project, much 'learning' occurred. To move the sustainability agenda on, targets must be set that are relevant and stretching, yet achievable for a given set of circumstances.

Equally important, progress must be monitored to ensure that targets are met. In addition to the Commission for a Sustainable London 2012, dedicated teams within the ODA, LOCOG and CLM and the contractors' environmental managers ensured that sustainability remained high on the agenda for the duration of the project. The OPLC faces a considerable challenge to maintain this momentum.

Because sustainability was embedded in its DNA, London 2012 nurtured innovation in many guises. Notable highlights related to the parkland include the extent of soil cleaning and reuse on the Olympic Park, a design based on hydrology, flood management and biodiverse habitats rather than formal herbaceous borders, and a pioneering water recycling treatment for its irrigation. In terms of construction, London 2012 pioneered site-wide energy distribution, exceptional design quality of infrastructure buildings, extensive trialling of low carbon concrete mixes and engagement with the supply chain to develop non-toxic products and increase recycling. Careful scrutiny of temporary procurement packages has significantly reduced the carbon footprint and waste related to staging the Games. The list goes on; these successes and many more have filled the pages of this book.

Could the Games have been more sustainable? Yes. Disappointments are inevitable when ambition is high. The signature Aquatics Centre, whose design was instrumental in winning the bid, could have been leaner had sustainability driven the brief at competition stage, yet the solution of the temporary wings was an intelligent one to sizing the building more appropriately for legacy. The Stadium, noteworthy for its lightweight design, could have been further future-proofed for the likely conversion to a permanent sports venue, a use that was apparent from the outset, even though there was no confirmed legacy operator at the time. But designing for legacy means spending more upfront, which is at odds with the short-termism of a one-off mega-event with a fixed budget. The need to spend more to ensure future flexibility was most apparent in the challenges of delivering the IBC although flexibility for the building's use in legacy was an important design consideration from the outset. In this multimedia digital age of Twitter and instantaneous newscasts, a press installation of a scale that speaks of yesteryear may no longer be required.

The demise of the wind turbine is a dual disappointment because of its role as a potent symbol and renewable energy provider. Yet the ODA's subsequent commitment to invest in energy efficiency in nearby schools and housing is a welcome alternative that will bring immediate and tangible improvements to the surrounding community. The hope was that such a turbine on the Olympic Park site could set a precedent for more such large-scale urban turbines across Britain. That will have to wait.

Although the scale of the Village can seem imposing in its current context within the parklands, its design is a reflection of its longer-term place in the Stratford City masterplan. After the Games, the Village will be quickly transformed in to 2,818 homes, with 50% designated as affordable housing.

The very design of the blocks is borne from the strong belief that this type of high-density living is the most sustainable model for urban growth. While the OPLC's early proposals for low-rise family housing on the Park's remaining development sites offer a more balanced

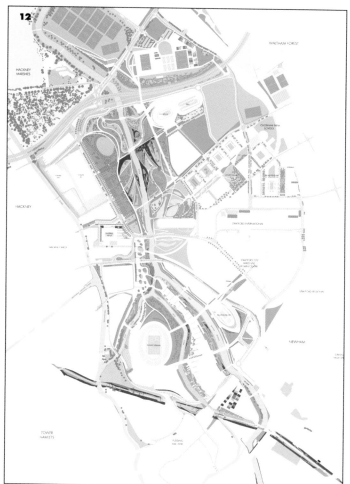

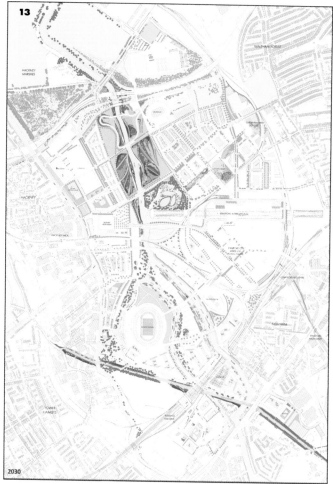

model to integrate with the existing community, it is the Village that will form the dense neighbourhood centre. The development also includes a Polyclinic, Chobham Academy and over 16ha of green roof space.

Building a residential development of this scale, in the timeframe set by the Games, set a difficult challenge for delivering the ODA's sustainability targets. This challenge was amplified by the budget constraints that were necessitated by the tightening of the credit market midway through the project. However, the development was still able to achieve the Code for Sustainable Homes Level 4, and is the first high-density development to do so. It also achieved a major success in energy efficiency, with an average 80% improvement over the 2006 Part L building regulations. This will reduce the carbon footprint of the development, as well as significantly reducing utility bills for the occupants.

The management of the Village, the programming of its public realm and a rental policy that favours owner-occupiers over investors are current unknowns that, if handled with finesse,

11 The London Cable Car will link North Greenwich Arena in Greenwich with ExCeL in the Royal Docks in a 5 minute journey.

12 Post Games Transformation Plan 2013. A £300 million transformation budget immediately after the Games will remove the overlay and significantly increase the parkland. Grey areas are future development sites. This map is indicative only.

13 Legacy Masterplan 2030. Proposed new housing in the Park to be built out during the decades following the Games include areas south of the Velodrome, east of the IBC/MPC Complex, south of the Handball Arena and surrounding the Olympic Stadium. This map is indicative only.

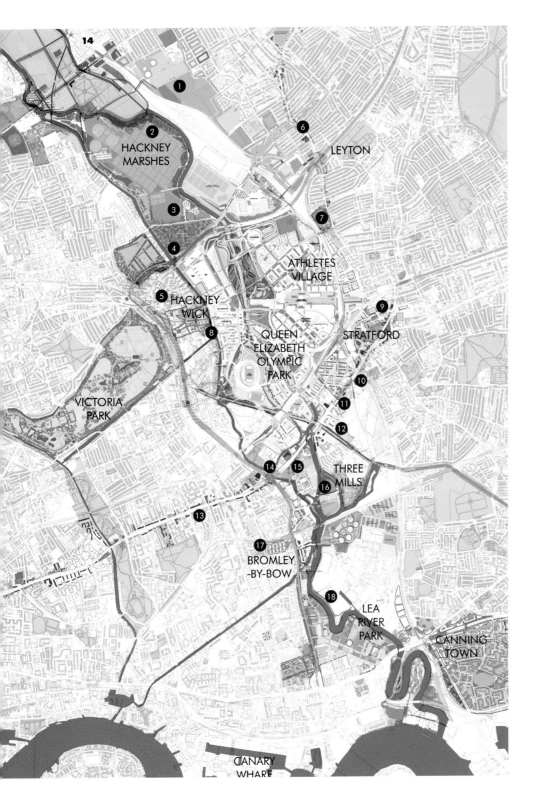

14 Emerging proposals for the Lea Valley. Map of both public and private development initiatives near the Olympic Park.

15 Olympic Fringe Masterplans. Six fringe masterplans, initiated in 2007, developed proposals for the neighbourhoods surrounding the Park.

16 Redevelopment of King's Cross Station. Refurbishment includes a new western concourse with an undulating glass canopy that was brought forward to be ready for summer 2012.

1. Marsh Lane

2. Hackney Marshes landscaping

3. Hackney Marshes Centre

4. Folly For a Flyover

5. Hackney Wick and Fish Island public realm

6. Leyton Links

7. Drapers Field

8. White Building

9. Stratford Town Centre

10. Stratford High Street DLR Station

11. Stratford High Street

12. Greenway

13. High Street 2012

14. Bow Riverside Path

15. Sugarhouse Studio

16. Three Mills Green

17. St Andrew's Phase

18. Fatwalk

could positively shape the Village's future. The extensive open space, proximity to public transport, and thoughtful architectural treatment of the buildings are all positives that will contribute to securing the Village's future as the surrounding development sites fill in.

The parallel planning application of Stratford City has complicated the London 2012 project, but the proximity of Westfield's retail and leisure offer is certain to create a synergy with the Park, attracting many newcomers to Stratford. In the long term, the nearby location and activity of Westfield, not to mention its many jobs, is sure to benefit the Park. An outdoor pedestrian route through to the Park has been maintained, and the visual drama of the Aquatics Centre and the attraction of ascending the Orbit are likely to draw shoppers, particularly on sunny days. Careful programming of activities and other uses that encourage residents of surrounding neighbourhoods to visit the Park after the Games will be needed to promote it as a community resource for all.

INFLUENCING BEHAVIOUR

Despite these many challenges, it is clear that London 2012 has pushed the definition of a sustainable Games to the next level. Its sustainability agenda has engaged with numerous stakeholders and audiences. Most immediate are the Host Boroughs and surrounding communities on the threshold of the Olympic Park. Radical change has altered the physical

fabric of east London. The burning question now is how that will impact the social and economic opportunities of local residents. Improved transport links, the Olympic Park and the Village housing are the physical building blocks of regeneration, but they must be followed with investment in employment training, job creation, schools and health facilities if residents of the East End are to achieve convergence with fellow Londoners.

Equally immediate is the impact of the Games' low carbon building programme on the UK construction industry. The ODA's sustainability targets, together with designer workshops, responsible procurement and a requirement for an environmental manager on every site, have created a culture of sustainability that has raised awareness across all project teams, on construction sites and with supply chains. The ODA has documented this process with over 300 'learning legacy' papers, of which about 30 deal directly with environmental issues in construction (www.London2012.com/LearningLegacy). Those touched directly by the programme are likely to transmit more sustainable ways of working to colleagues and co-workers. The UK Green Building Council, designated an official partner for knowledge capture from London 2012, will run numerous educational events for its cross-industry membership.

The planning of Rio 2016 will also benefit from the London experience through the IOC Host-to-Host agreement to share best practice. Rio's urban context and most pressing environmental issues are different: transport, sewage treatment, water and protection of the natural environment are top priorities. Carbon is a less important driver because approximately 90 per cent of Brazil's electricity is generated by hydropower, and almost half its vehicles are powered by ethanol.

Much can, however, be learned from the organisational structure and process that underpin London 2012's commitment to sustainability – from high-level leadership to environmental site managers with external auditing. A dedicated sustainability team must set realistic targets tailored to the Brazilian context in order to achieve practical outcomes. The extension of public transport to Barra de Tijuca where the Olympic Park is located would be a major legacy achievement. Reduction of waste on construction sites is another important issue where the Rio Games could catalyse immediate change. Sustainable building benchmarks have yet to be developed so the design of the Games venues offers an opportunity to develop pilot projects that can form the basis for low carbon building regulations.

By far the widest audience for the Games and by far the most difficult to influence is the general public: Londoners who have witnessed the building of the Olympic Park and venues, the British public who will play host to nearly 15,000 athletes, hundreds of thousands of spectators and the global television audience, estimated at 4 billion viewers. Though entertaining, the BBC comedy series *Twenty Twelve* has done sustainability a disservice by marginalising it to a discussion of wind turbines and recycling.

The Games themselves offer an ideal vehicle to communicate London 2012's wide-ranging environmental successes. In order to support all the good work that has been done, sustainability must be made manifest in every detail: from the dressing of historic London to food and drink offerings and sponsors' merchandising. The ecological design of the Olympic Park and its new low carbon venues are testament to the fact that controlling the built environment is easier than influencing human behaviour.

17 Visualisation of Olympic Park in legacy. View looking south towards Canary Wharf with the Olympic Stadium and Anish Kapoor's Orbit tower (centre left) and the converted press buildings (right foreground) surrounded by new terraced housing. This image is indicative only.

Team Credits

The Greenway
Architect: Adams & Sutherland
Engineering and Project Management: Arup
Landscaping: Jonathan Cook Landscape
Architects
Lead Contractor: Volker FitzPatrick
Architects (The View Tube): Urban Space
Management

Landscaping the Olympic Park
Design: LDA Design and Hargreaves
Associates (from Stage D)
Aecom/EDAW (through Stage C)
Biodiversity Action Plan: EDAW/Gary Grant
and LDA /Atkins [CLM]
Engineering: Atkins / Arup
Lead Contractors: Bam Nuttall / Skanska
Planting Design: James Hitchmough and
Nigel Dunnett, University of Sheffield
Planting Design: Sarah Price Landscapes
Soil and Landscape Consultancy: Tim O'Hare
Associates
Trees: Hilliers Nurseries
Wetland plants: Salix
2012 Gardens plants: Palmstead Nurseries
2012 Gardens planting:Willerby Landscapes

Central Bridge
Architect: Heneghan Peng Architects
Structural Engineer: Adams Kara Taylor
Lead Contractor: Lagan Construction

Olympic Stadium
Architect: Populous
Lead Contractor: Sir Robert McAlpine
Structural and Services Engineer: Buro
Happold
Landscape Architect: Hyland Edgar Driver

Aquatics Centre
Architect: Zaha Hadid Architects
Lead Contractor: Balfour Beatty
Sports Architect: S+P Architects
Engineering: Arup
Steel roof construction: Rowecord

Velodrome
Architect: Hopkins Architects
Lead Contractor: ISG plc
Structural Engineer: Expedition Engineering
Services Engineer: BDSP Partnership
Track Designer: Ron Webb
Landscape: Grant Associates

Handball Arena
Architect: MAKE
Sports Architect: PTW
Detailed design: Populous
Engineers: Arup
Structural Engineer: Sinclair Knight Merz
Lead Contractor: Buckingham Group
Contracting

Eton Manor
Architect: Stanton Williams
Engineers: Arup
Main contractors: Mansell Construction
Services, PJ Careys, Slick Seating Systems,
Mitie Engineering, A&T, Nussli

Basketball Arena
Architect: Wilkinson Eyre Architects
Sports Architect: KSS
Engineers: Arup
Structural Engineer: Sinclair Knight Merz
Main contractors: Barr Construction, Slick
Seating, Base, Mitie, Envirowrap, Volker
Fitzpatrick, and McAvoy

Water Polo Arena
Architect: David Morley Architects
Structural Engineer: Buro Happold
Environmental Engineer: Max Fordham
Main contractors: ES Group, Jackson Civil
Engineering Group Ltd, Alto Seating Systems
Ltd, A&T/Barr & Wray, Byrne Group plc,
Balfour Beatty

Lee Valley White Water Centre
Architect: FaulknerBrowns Architects
Structural and Services Engineers: Cundall
White Water Course Specialists: Whitewater
Parks International
Landscape Designers: Michael van
Valkenburgh Associates
Lead Contractor: Morrison Construction

INFRASTRUCTURE BUILDINGS

Primary Substation
Architect: NORD Architecture
Structural Engineers: Andrews Associates
Building Services: Applied Energy
Main Contractor: EDF Energy Contracting
Contractor: Kier

Olympic Park Energy Centre and Stratford Energy Centre
Architect: John McAslan + Partners
Structural Engineer: Adams, Kara Taylor
Main Contractor: P.J. Carey
Owner and operator: Cofely, a subsidiary of GDF Suez

Pudding Mill Lane Pumping Station
Architect: John Lyall Architects (now Lyall Bills & Young)
Structural and Services Engineer: Hyder Consulting
Utilities Contractor: Barhale
Building Contractor: Hutton Construction

Old Ford Water Recycling Plant
Architect: Lyall Bills & Young (formerly John Lyall Architects)
Contractor/ Engineer: Black and Veatch Ltd

Old Ford Ground Water Pumping Station
Architect: Lyall Bills & Young (formerly John Lyall Architects)
Main Contractor: Morrisons Construction
Structural/ Services Engineer: Frankham Consultancy Group Limited

Stratford Box
Architect: Lyall Bills & Young (formerly John Lyall Architects)
Structural/ Services Engineer: Frankham Consultancy Group Limited
Lead Contractor: Morrisons Construction

OTHER PARK BUILDINGS

IBC/MPC Complex
Architects: International Broadcast Centre (IBC): Allies & Morrison, RPS: Envelope design
Main Press Centre (MPC): Allies & Morrison
Structural and Services Engineers: Buro Happold
Landscape: Townshend Landscape Architects
Lead Contractor: Carillion

Olympic and Paralympic Village
Architects: Fletcher Priest Architects (masterplanning)
Allford Hall Monaghan Morris/Patel Taylor (residential masterplanning)
Vogt (landscape concept design)

Stratford City
Architects: Arup (urban design), Fletcher Priest Architects, West 8, Allford Hall Monaghan Morris (AHMM), Niall McLaughlin Architects, Eric Parry Architects
Structural Engineers (p. 205): URS (N01, N02), Robert Bird (N03, N04, N07, N15) AKT (N09, N10)
M&E: Wallace Whittle (N01, N02, N03, N04, N11), Hilson Moran (N07), Hoare Lea (N09, N10, N15), Buro Happold (N12)
Infrastructure, Utilities, Wind Engineer, Vertical Transport, Waste, Environment/ Sustainability, Geotechnical, Daylight (all sitewide): Arup
Access Consultant: David Bonnett Associates
Traffic Engineer (site wide): WSP
Cost Consultant (site wide): Gardiner & Theobald
Landscape (site wide): Vogt
Ecological Design: Biodiversity by Design

Chobham Academy
Architect: Allford Hall Monaghan Morris (AHMM)
Structural Engineer: Adams Kara Taylor
Services Engineer: Buro Happold / Hoare Lea
Landscape Architect: Kinnear Landscape Architects
Lead Contractor: BAM Construction

Polyclinic
Architect: Penoyre & Prasad
Structural Engineers: WSP
Services Engineers: Wallace Whittle
Landscape Architects: Applied Landscape Design
Lead Contractor: Willmott Dixon

APPENDIX 1
KEY PLAYERS AND STAKEHOLDERS

KEY PLAYERS

London Organising Committee of the Olympic Games and Paralympic Games (LOCOG)
LOCOG is responsible for preparing, staging and hosting a memorable Games in London in 2012 and fulfilling the sustainability pledge made in the bid.

Olympic Delivery Authority (ODA)
The ODA is the public body responsible for designing and building the new venues and infrastructure for the Games and their use after 2012. The ODA is also responsible for making sure the construction project sets new standards for sustainable development

CLM
The ODA appointed CLM Delivery Partner (a consortium specially formed for the Games made up of CH2M Hill, Laing O'Rourke and Mace) to act as programme manager for design, procurement and construction supervision throughout the project.

Olympic Park Legacy Company (OPLC)
The OPLC is charged with assisting the Government and the Mayor of London in fulfilling the legacy promises made in the bid and securing the timely development of the Olympic Park site as a high- quality and sustainable mixed community

MAJOR STAKEHOLDERS

Department for Culture, Media and Sport (DCMS), responsible for maximising the economic, social, health and environmental benefits the Games bring to the United Kingdom

Greater London Authority (GLA), responsible for maximising the economic, social, health and environmental benefits the Games bring to all Londoners.

London Development Agency (LDA), responsible for leading the land acquisition activity on the Olympic Park site

London Boroughs of Greenwich, Hackney, Newham, Tower Hamlets, and Waltham Forest, Barking and Dagenham
the six Host Boroughs

Lee Valley Regional Park Authority, a significant land owner/operator

Transport for London (TfL) and other transport delivery agencies (Network Rail, Highways, Agency, and BAA), responsible for transport improvements

OTHER STAKEHOLDERS

Strategic Forum for Construction
Construction Products Association
Building Research Establishment
WWF and BioRegional
Environment Agency
British Waterways
Commission for a Sustainable London 2012

APPENDIX 2
LIST OF INTERVIEWEES

Interviews were conducted by the author between November 2010 and June 2011

5th Studio
Tom Holbrook

Adams & Sutherland
Graeme Sutherland

AECOM
Jason Prior

Allford, Hall, Monaghan, Morris (AHMM)
Simon Allford
Jon Brent
Philip Turner

Allies & Morrison
Paul Appleton
Bob Allies
Graham Morrison
Paul Summerlin
Eddie Taylor

Architectural Association
Joana Goncalvez

Architectural Review + The Architects' Journal
Paul Finch

Arup
Emmanuelle Danisi
Mike King
Mike Stych

Atkins
Ian Mead
Julian Sutherland

BDSP Engineers
Klaus Bode
Gustavo Brunelli

BioRegional
Susan Riddleton

Jill Savery
Chloe Souque (seconded Carillion)

Buro Happold
Ian Guest

CLM Delivery Partner
Samantha Connelly
Tim Wright

Commission for a Sustainable London
Shaun McCarthy

Cundall
Damien Dungworth

David Morley Architects
David Morley

Design for London (now OPLC)
Eleanor Fawcett

Dorrington Property
Alan Leibowitz

Expedition Engineering
Andy Weir

FaulknerBrowns Architects
Michael Hall
Peter Mouncey

Fletcher Priest Architects
Jonathan Kendall

Heneghan Peng Architects
Andreas Dopfer

Glenn Howells Architects
Tom Griffiths
Frank Otto

Hopkins Architects
Chris Bannister
Mike Taylor

ISG
Simon Attwood
Tim Sullivan

John Lyall Architects
Chris Bills

Hlynur Jakobsson
John Lyall

John McAslan + Partners
Kevin Lloyd
Arran Pexton

KLH Sustainability
Kirsten Henson, formerly CLM

LDA Design
Neil Mattinson

Lend Lease
Andrew Kinsey

Lifschutz, Davidson Sandilands
Alex Lifschutz

London Organising Committee of the Olympic Games and Paralympic Games (LOCOG)
Amanda Aukett
Phil Cumming
Kevin Owens
David Stubbs

London School of Economics
Ricky Burdett – Chief Advisor on Architecture and Urbanism, ODA (2006–2010); Advisor on Legacy Master Plan, OPLC (2006–)
Juliet Davis

MAKE
Stuart Fraser

NORD
Alan Pert

Olympic Delivery Authority (ODA)
Dan Epstein
Jerome Frost
Margaret Hickish
John Hopkins
Richard Jackson
Selina Mason
Alison Nimmo

Olympic Park Legacy Company (OPLC)
Niall McNevin, formerly ODA

Penoyre & Prasad
Ian Goodfellow
Mark Rowe

Populous
Philip Johnson
Jeff Keas
Rod Sheard

Robert Maguire Consulting
Robert Maguire

Sinclair Knight Merz
Nick Link

Southfacing
Ben Cartmell

Speirs + Major
Mark Speirs

Stanton Williams
Rawden Pettitt

UK-GBC
Paul King
Anna Surgenor, formerly ODA

UK Power Networks
Liam O'Sullivan

Westfield
John Burton

Wilkinson Eyre
Jim Eyre
Sam Wright

WWF
Simon Lewis

Zaha Hadid Architects
Jim Heverin

Reviewers
ODA: Simon Wright, Holly Knight, Ruari Maybank
CLM: Caroline Richards, Christian Bonnard

BIBLIOGRAPHY

The vast majority of the research for this book took the form of interviews with individuals at LOCOG, the ODA and the OPLC and design team members for the various projects. Stage D design documents, in particular the sustainability statements, were also a key source of information.

BioRegional, CLM, Atkins, *Reuse and Recycling on the London 2012 Olympic Park: Lessons for Demolition, Construction and Regeneration*, April 2010

Commission for a Sustainable London 2012, *Annual Review 2010*, April 2011

Davis, Juliet, *Urbanising the Event: how past processes, present politics and future plans shape London's Olympic Legacy*, London School of Economics & Political Science (unpublished PhD thesis), 2011

Department of Communities and Local Government, *Population churn and its impact on socio-economic convergence in the five London 2012 host boroughs*, 2010

Fry, Tony, 'Sydney's Green Games?', *Architecture Australia*, Sep/October 1997

Greater London Authority, *Olympic Park Legacy Company: Proposals by the Mayor of London for public consultation*, February 2011

Greenpeace, *China after the Olympics: Lessons from Beijing*, 2008

Greenpeace, *Sydney Olympics Scorecard*, 2000

Hampton, Janie, *The Austerity Olympics: When the Games Came to London in 1948*, Aurum, 2008

Hargreaves, George, Julia Czerniak, Anita Berrizbeitia and Liz Campbell Kelly, *The Alchemy of Landscape Architecture*, Thames & Hudson, 2009

LOCOG in collaboration with Atkins, *Temporary Materials Guidelines, 2010*, www.london2012.com/documents/locog-publications/2012-temporary-materials.pdf

LOCOG Venues and Infrastructure with Team Populous, Kit of Parts, August 2010, rev. ed.

London 2012, *Sustainability Plan*, 2nd ed., December 2009

London 2012, *Sustainability Policy*, October 2007

London Borough of Newham, *Olympic Legacy Lessons*, 2010 http://www.thebigopportunity.org.uk/uploads/4/0/0/1/4001782/newham_symposium__olympic_legacy_lessons_march_20101.pdf

Olympic Delivery Authority, *Sustainable Development Strategy*, January 2007

Olympic Delivery Authority, *Sustainability Learning Legacy, Procurement & Use of Sustainable Concrete on the Olympic Park* by Kirsten Henson, January 2010

Olympic Park Energy Strategy by Dan Epstein, 2010

Olympic Park Legacy Company, *A Walk Around Queen Elizabeth Olympic Park*, 2010

Poynter, Gavin, and Iain MacRury, ed., *Olympic Cities: 2012 and the Remaking of London*, Ashgate, 2009

United Nations Environment Programme, *Beijing 2008 Olympic Games: An environmental review*

United Nations Environment Programme, *Independent Environmental Assessment: Beijing 2008 Olympic Games*, 2009 http://www.unep.org/pdf/BEIJING_REPORT_COMPLETE.pdf

WellMet 2050, University of Cambridge and Dan Epstein, Olympic Delivery Authority, *Reducing embodied carbon through energy efficient design*, Learning Legacy Case Study, May 2011

WWF-Greece, *Environmental Assessment of the Athens 2004 Olympic Games*, July 2004

KEY REPORTS

Countless reports from bid stage right through to staging the Games have addressed different aspects of sustainability. Both LOCOG and the ODA produced their own strategies and the Commission for a Sustainable London 2012 provided a monitoring function throughout. Some of the most significant are shown below.

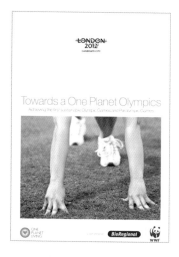

WWF and BioRegional **Towards a One Planet Olympics**, 2004

This seminal 7-page document formed the basis for the environmental chapter of the London 2012 bid document based on the concept of a One Planet Olympics.

Olympic Delivery Authority, **Sustainable Development Strategy**, January 2007.

This was the document which set out the environmental targets for the London 2012 venues.

LOCOG, **London 2012 Sustainability Plan** December 2009, 2nd ed.

This was the key LOCOG document which set out the five priority sustainability themes for delivering the Games: climate change, waste, biodiversity, inclusion and healthy living.

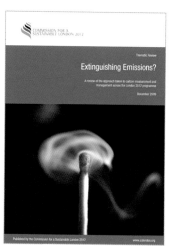

Commission for a Sustainable London 2012. A sampling of the numerous reports prepared by the Commission for a Sustainable London 2012 (CSL). CSL's monitoring role continues until 2013.

INDEX

Numbers in roman script refer to the text; numbers in italics refer to illustrations and the content of the captions

Old Ford Water Recycling Plant 178
Olympic Stadium 80, 81, 83, 84, *84–5*
Polyclinic 214, 216, *217*
Velodrome *104*, 109, *116–17*
West Ham Bus Depot *53*
see also green roofs
Rowe, Mark (Penoyre & Prasad), quoted 214
Royal Artillery barracks, Paralympic Archery relocated to 126, 128
RPS Group 186
IBC *187*, *195*, *196*
rubber floors, Chobham Academy 212
rush hour, alleviation after Games 51

S+P Architects 99
St Pancras, train connections 50
sand, reuse 227–8
Sarah Price Landscapes 66
schools
    Host Boroughs, energy efficiency measures 72
    Stratford City 200
    see also Chobham Academy
SDS (Sustainable Development Strategy) 36, 76, *254*
sea level rise, reducing impact 40
seating
    Aquatics Centre *75*, 88, 89–90, *92–3*, 96, 98, 99, *99*
    Basketball Arena 30, 132, 134, *140*, *141*
    Beach Volleyball 220, *227*
    Excel Centre *224*
    Handball Arena 120, *121*, 122, 123
    Lea River *57*
    Olympic Stadium 80–1, 84
    the overlay 220
    Velodrome 106
    Water Polo Arena 144
Secured by Design, standard 40
security fencing, Olympic Park Energy Centre 166
Seele (hot water systems) 94
sewage
    Beckton Sewage Treatment Works 170
    Olympic Park 58
    processing by Old Ford Water Recycling Plant 170, 176
    sewer network, Olympic Park 170
    and sustainable water 29
    treatment works, reduce flows 40
    see also Northern Outfall Sewer; waste; water, cleansing
SFC (Strategic Forum for Construction) 250
Sheard, Rod (Populous), quoted 78
Sheffield, University of, Department of Landscape 66
shopping *see* high street; Westfield Shopping Centre
short-termism, and design for legacy 243
shower demand, Aquatics Centre 96
signage *17*, 20–1, *175*, 241
    in pavement *21*
Sinclair Knight Merz (structural engineering firm) 124, 141
Singapore, IOC Session July 2005 11, 88
SIP (Structural Insulated Panels) 166, 167
site remediation 54–5
    see also soil, cleansing
Skanska 66
SKH Engineers, interviewees 252
skills *see* employment and skills
SKM Consulting 135
slag *see* GGBS

'Soho East' 188, *192*, *197*
soil
    cleansing operation 54–5, *54*, *55*, 243
        and landscaping of Olympic Park 56
    contaminated, minimising excavation 144
    from excavation of CTRL, and Stratford City 200
    reuse 243
    used in Olympic Park 63
Soil Hospital, Olympic Park *54*, *55*
solar lift (elevator) *243*
solar thermal technologies 70–1, 84
    Aquatics Centre 91
    Chobham Academy 212
    LVWWC 153, 156
    see also temperature control
Souque, Chloe (Carillion Sustainability Advisor), quoted 194
Southern Hemisphere 2012 Garden *63*
Southfacing, interviewee 252
spectators
    Olympic Stadium 13, 81
    transport to Games 50
    see also air travel; seating
Speirs + Major, interviewee 252
sporting venues, post-Games use 76, 126, 131, 234
sports activities programming, necessity for 241
sports injuries, treatment 214
sports venues
    remaining after Games 234
    see also individual venues
stadia, embodied carbon emissions and embodied energy studies *81*
Stadium Island 84
Stanton Williams Architects 128, 252
    see also Eton Manor; Hackney Marshes Centre
steel
    considered for Velodrome roof 109
    reflected light, Central Bridge *62*
    use in Aquatics Centre 89
    use in Olympic Stadium construction 80, *80*, 82
    see also Cor-ten steel
stent 100, 194
'stitches' (connections to adjacent neighbourhoods) 66
Stoke Mandeville Games 12
Strategic Forum for Construction, as stakeholder 250
Stratford
    Station 50, 151
    transport infrastructure 50
Stratford Box 182, *182*, *183*
Stratford City 200–2
    energy provision 68
    masterplan 51, *202*, *204*, *205*, *208*, 245
    post-Games 237
    power plant to serve 164
    Vogt proposal 198
Stratford Energy Centre 164–8
    see also energy centres
Stratford International rail station 50, *50*
    and IBC/MPC Complex 186
Structural Insulated Panels (SIP) 166, 167
Stubbs, David (LOCOG Head of Sustainability), quoted 24
studios, in IBC/MPC Complex Neon scheme 188
Substation *see* Primary Substation
SuDS (Sustainable Drainage Systems),

drainage blocks 56, 59
Sugar House Lane 236
Summerlin, Paul (Allies and Morrison), quoted 189, 190
sunpipes, Handball Arena *71*, 120, *120*, 122–3, *122*
supply chains p21
    aggregate in Aquatics Centre 105
    early engagement, Water Polo Arena 144, 146, 148–9
    and innovation 228
    sustainability 222, 243, 248
    sustainable materials 29, 30
    temporary structures 76
    timber 39, 64, 207
    Water Polo Arena 144, 146, 148, 149
sustainability
    assessing 242–7
    awareness raising 28
    British Standard 8901 11
    as central role 14, 28, 52, 76, 248
    defining 11, 13
    disappointments 243
    monitoring 30
    organigram *37*
    organisational structure and process 248
    overlay design 222
    public awareness 220
    sustainable aspirations 30, 34
    sustainable urban quarter for East London 13, 73
    'walk in the park' 230
Sustainability Policy, London 2012 Games 34
sustainability working group, LOCOG 228
Sustainable Development Strategy 36, 76, *254*
Sustainable Development Strategy (ODA report) *254*
Sustainable Urban Drainage Systems 16, 59
Sustainable? Naturally ... 255
Sutherland, Graeme (Adams & Sutherland), quoted 16, 19
swimming pools
    Olympic-standard, London 86
    in previous Games 89
    temporary, Eton Manor 126
    see also Aquatics Centre
Sydney 2000 Games
    embodied carbon *24*
    environmental profile 24
    lack of environmental targets 30
    legacy planning 24
    lessons learned 24, 89
    masterplan, and Homebush Bay development 24
    Olympic Park 24, *27*, 34, 58, 78
syngas plant 236

taps, low-flow 228
target metrics 11
targets 243
    carbon dioxide emissions, reduction targets 36, 39, 68, 72, 207
    ecological 40, 46
    energy 36, 39, 68–71
    environmental 11, 24
    ODA 12, 19–20, 34, 37, 68
    renewable energy 36
    sustainability 30
    waste and water reduction 39
Tarmac 83
Tate Modern (previously Bankside Power Station) *164*
technological advances

and energy centres 164
Old Ford Water Recycling Plant 176, 178
technologies
    limited to proven technologies 68
    renewable 39, *71*, 72
        Sydney Games 22
    water-saving 39
television
    and Aquatics Centre 98
    studios, as possible end-use for IBC 191
    and sunpipes in Handball Arena 122–3
temperature control
    Aquatics Centre 90, 91, 94, *98*
    Chobham Academy 210
    different demands 68
    Handball Arena *123*
    IBC 191
    LVWWC 153, 156
    MPC *192*
    Olympic Park 68, 70
    the overlay 225
    Polyclinic 214, 216
    tents and cabins in the overlay 223
    Velodrome 106, 108, 110–11
    Water Polo Arena 146
    see also CCHP; CHP; district heating; HVAC; solar thermal technologies
temporary, definition extended 227
Temporary Materials Guidelines 222
temporary structures, after the Games 235
temporary venues
    conversion to permanent building 84
    historic London settings 220
    if long-term uses not justified 73
    underlying premise 141
    use for 2012 Games 11
temporary versus permanent 11, 19, 36, 80
tennis
    balls, reuse 228
    centre, Eton Manor, post-Games 126, 131
    courts, temporary for Games *129*
    hall, Eton Manor *128*, *130*
Tensotherm 148
tents
    use in the overlay 220
    The Village 220
TfL *see* Transport for London (TfL)
Thames, River, sewage treatment p43, 159, 170
Thames Water
    and design of Old Ford Water Recycling Plant 176
    design partnership with ODA 178
    and The Greenway 16, 20
    and infrastructure buildings 158
    Old Ford Ground Water Pumping Station 180
    outline design for Pudding Mill Lane Pumping Station 170
    as potential funding partner for water recycling treatment plant 60
    View Tube 22
Thijsse, J.P. 63
ticket turnstiles, Olympic Stadium, location 84
tickets, number available 10, 13
tidal energy 71
Tim O'Hare Associates 66
timber
    in Aquatics Centre 88, *92–3*, 98
    audit trail 39, 64, 207
    for benches 64
    in Equestrian platform, Greenwich Park *222*

PICTURE CREDITS

p. 2: © Edmund Sumner; pp. 6–7: © Edmund Sumner; p. 9: © London Organising Committee of the Olympic Games and Paralympic Games Ltd (Allies & Morrison Architects); p. 10: © Jason Orton; p. 11: 3. © Design for London; p. 11: 4. © Design for London; pp. 12–13: © Olympic Delivery Authority; p. 14: 6. © Olympic Delivery Authority; p. 14: 7. © Edmund Sumner; p. 14. 8. © Edmund Sumner; p. 15. © Olympic Park Legacy Company, 2011. This image is indicative only; p. 17: © Edmund Sumner; p. 18: © Adams & Sutherland; p. 19: © Adams & Sutherland; p. 20: © Adams & Sutherland; p. 21: all © Edmund Sumner; pp. 22–3: both © Edmund Sumner; p. 24: 21. © Populous; p. 24: 22. © WellMet 2050, University of Cambridge; p. 25: © Allies & Morrison; p. 26: © Populous; p. 27: © CORBIS; p. 28: © Olympic Delivery Authority; p. 29: © BioRegional; p. 30: © Edmund Sumner; p. 31: © Edmund Sumner; pp. 32–3: © Edmund Sumner; p. 35: © Edmund Sumner; p. 36: © Richard Davies; p. 37: © Laura Mark; p. 38: © Edmund Sumner (halo lighting mast designed by Philips); p. 42: © Populous; p. 43: 35. © Best Foot Forward for LOCOG; p. 43: 36. © WellMet, University of Cambridge for the ODA; p. 45: © Olympic Delivery Authority, 2005; p. 47: © AECOM and Populous; p. 48: © AECOM; p. 49: both © AECOM; p. 50: © Allies & Morrison; p. 51: © Edmund Sumner; p. 52: © Olympic Delivery Authority; p. 53: © Morley von Sternberg (Bus Depot designed by PringleRichardsSharratt); p. 54: both © Olympic Delivery Authority; p. 55: © Olympic Delivery Authority; p. 57: © Olympic Delivery Authority; p. 58: © ARUP; p. 59: 15. © AECOM; p. 59: 16. © John Lyall Architects; p. 60: © Edmund Sumner (landscaping by Atkins (river edge engineer) with LDA Design and Hargreaves Associates); p. 61: 18. © Heneghan Peng; p. 61: 19. © Edmund Sumner; p. 62: 20. © Edmund Sumner (Central Bridge constructed by Heneghan Peng and Arup); p. 62: 21. © LDA Design and Hargreaves Associates; p. 63: © Edmund Sumner (landscaping by LDA Design and Hargreaves Associates with Sara Price); p. 64: 23. © Edmund Sumner; p. 65: 24. © LDA Design; p. 66: © Edmund Sumner; p. 67: © Edmund Sumner; p. 68: © Edmund Sumner; p. 69: 28. © Olympic Delivery Authority/ London Organising Committee of the Olympic Games and Paralympic Games Ltd ; p. 69. 29: © Edmund Sumner; p. 70: © Olympic Delivery Authority; p. 71: both © Edmund Sumner; p. 72: 33. © Edmund Sumner; p. 72: 34. © ARUP; p. 73: © Olympic Delivery Authority; p. 75: © Edmund Sumner; p. 77: © Olympic Delivery Authority; p. 79: © Populous; p. 80: © Edmund Sumner; p. 81: both © Populous; p. 82: 7. © Edmund Sumner; p. 82: 8. © Populous; p. 83: © Populous; pp. 84–5: © Edmund Sumner; p. 87: © Edmund Sumner; p. 88: © courtesy of Zaha Hadid Architects; p. 89: © MillerHare/Bennetts Associates; p. 90: © Edmund Sumner; p. 91: © ARUP; pp. 92–3: © Edmund Sumner; p. 94: © courtesy of Zaha Hadid Architects; p. 95: both © courtesy of Zaha Hadid Architects; p. 96: © Olympic Delivery Authority; p. 97: © Edmund Sumner; p. 98: © ARUP; p. 99: 23. © Olympic Delivery Authority; p. 99. 24: © Edmund Sumner; p. 101: © Edmund Sumner; p. 102: © Edmund Sumner; p. 103: © Edmund Sumner; p. 104: © Edmund Sumner; p. 105: both © Edmund Sumner; p. 107: © Edmund Sumner; p. 108: © Richard Davies; p. 109: 33. © Hopkins Architects; p. 109: 34. © Olympic Delivery Authority; p. 110: © Olympic Delivery Authority; p. 111: 36. © Hopkins Architects; p. 111: 37. © BDSP; p. 112: both © BDSP; p. 113: © BDSP; p. 114: © Edmund Sumner; p. 115: © Edmund Sumner; pp. 116–17: © Edmund Sumner; p. 119: © Edmund Sumner; p. 120: 45. © MAKE; p. 120: 46: © Edmund Sumner; p. 121: ©

Edmund Sumner; p. 122: © Edmund Sumner; p. 123: both © MAKE; p. 124: both © MAKE; p. 125: both © MAKE; p. 127: © Stanton Williams Architects; p. 128: both © Stanton Williams Architects; p. 129: both © Stanton Williams Architects; p. 130: © Stanton Williams Architects; p. 131: © Stanton Williams Architects; p. 133: © Edmund Sumner; p. 134: © Wilkinson Eyre Architects; p. 135: 64. © Olympic Delivery Authority; p. 135: 65. © Edmund Sumner; p. 136: 66. © Edmund Sumner; p. 136: 67. © Wilkinson Eyre Architects; p. 137: © Wilkinson Eyre Architects; p. 138: © Wilkinson Eyre Architects; p. 139: © Edmund Sumner; p. 140: © Edmund Sumner; p. 141: both © Edmund Sumner; pp. 142–3: © Edmund Sumner; p. 145: © Edmund Sumner; p. 146: © David Morley Architects; p. 147: © David Morley Architects; p. 148: © David Morley Architects; p. 149: © David Morley Architects; p. 151: © FaulknerBrowns Architects; p. 152: © FaulknerBrowns Architects; p. 153: 82. © FaulknerBrowns Architects; p. 153: 83. © Cundall; pp. 154–5: © FaulknerBrowns Architects; pp. 156–7: all © FaulknerBrowns Architects; pp. 158–9: © Edmund Sumner; p. 161: © Edmund Sumner; p. 162: © Olympic Delivery Authority; p. 163: 92. © Edmund Sumner; p. 163: 93. © NORD Architecture; p. 165: © Edmund Sumner; p. 166: both © John McAslan & Partners; p. 167: © Edmund Sumner; pp. 168–9: © John McAslan & Partners; p. 169: © Edmund Sumner; p. 171: © Edmund Sumner; p. 172: © John Lyall Architects; p. 173: both © John Lyall Architects; p. 174: both © John Lyall Architects; p. 175: 106. © Edmund Sumner; p. 175: 109. © John Lyall Architects; p. 177: © John Lyall Architects; pp. 178–9: all © John Lyall Architects; pp. 180–1: both © John Lyall Architects; pp. 182–3: both © John Lyall Architects; pp. 184–5: © (2011) clickclickjim; p. 187: © Edmund Sumner; pp. 188–9: both © Allies & Morrison; pp. 190–1: all © Allies & Morrison; p. 192: © Olympic Delivery Authority; p. 193: © Carillion/Igloo; p. 194: both © Allies & Morrison; p. 195: © RPS; p. 196: © RPS; p. 197: © (2011) clickclickjim; pp. 198–9: © Edmund Sumner; p. 201: © Edmund Sumner; p. 202: © AHMM; p. 203: 134. AHMM; p. 203: 135. © Niall McLaughlin Architects; p. 204: © Fletcher Priest Architects; p. 205: 137. © Fletcher Priest Architects; p. 205: 138. © Olympic Delivery Authority; p. 206: © Olympic Delivery Authority; p. 207: both © Edmund Sumner; p. 209: © Tim Soar; p. 210: © AHMM; p. 211: 144. © Tim Soar; p. 211: 145. © AHMM; p. 212: © Tim Soar; p. 213: both © AHMM; p. 215: © Penoyre & Prasad; p. 216: © Penoyre & Prasad; p. 217: © Penoyre & Prasad; p. 219: © Andy Hooper / Daily Mail / Solo Syndication; p. 221: © 2011 Getty Images; p. 222: © 2011 Getty Images; p. 223: © Populous/ Allies & Morrison; p. 224: © Populous; p. 225: © Edmund Sumner; p. 226: © Populous; p. 227: © 2011 Getty Images; pp. 228–9: © Edmund Sumner; p. 230: both © Lifschutz; p. 231: © 2011 Getty Images; p. 233: © Lend Lease; p. 234: © Edmund Sumner; p. 235: © 5th Studio; p. 236: © Allies & Morrison; p. 237: © Stanton Williams Architects; pp. 238–9: © Edmund Sumner; p. 240: © Stanton Williams Architects; p. 241: © Edmund Sumner; p. 242: © Adams & Sunderland; p. 243: © Matthew Lloyd Architects; p. 244: © Wilkinson Eyre; p. 245: both © Olympic Park Legacy Company, 2011. These images are indicative only; p. 246: © Design for London; p. 247: 15. © Design for London; p. 247: 16. © John McAslan & Partners; p. 249: © Olympic Park Legacy Company, 2011. This image is indicative only; p. 255: (top row left): © WWF and BioRegional; (top row middle): © Olympic Delivery Authority; (top row right): © LOCOG; (bottom row): all © Commission for a Sustainable London.